"There I Was . . ."
25 Years

Bob Stevens

TAB AERO

Blue Ridge Summit, PA

This book is dedicated to
the thousands of airmen
in *all* services since World War I,
who turned to humor and song
to make their task easier.

The cartoons in this book originally appeared in *Air Force* magazine, published by the Air Force Association. Compilations of selected cartoons were subsequently published in the books *"There I Was...,"* More *"There I Was...,"* *"There I Was Flat on My Back,"* and *"If You Read Me, Rock the Tower."* A hardcover edition of *"There I Was..." 25 Years* was published by The Village Press, 1990.

FIRST EDITION
THIRD PRINTING

Library of Congress Cataloging-in-Publication Data

Stevens, Bob, 1923-
      There I was— 25 years / Bob Stevens.
          p.   cm.
      Originally published: 1st ed. Bonsall, CA : Village Press, c1990.
      ISBN 0-8306-3831-8 (pbk.)
      1. Aeronautics—Caricatures and cartoons.   2. American wit and humor. Pictorial.   3. Air Force magazine.   I. Title.
  [NC1429.S64A4   1992]
  741.5'973—dc20   91-36163
                                                                        CIP

Acknowledgments

THE AUTHOR WISHES TO EXTEND GRATEFUL THANKS to all those who helped him in preparation of this book. Especially, I want to thank Richard M. Skinner, Jeff Rhodes, and Pearlie Draughn of *Air Force* magazine. Kudos go to Capt. George Cully and the people at the Air Force Historical Research Center, Maxwell AFB, for their cooperation and assistance. Also thanks to A.T. Lloyd, Boeing Airplane Co., and national vice president for the Air Force Association's northwest region, who was instrumental in obtaining the unit insignia that were displayed in the first edition of this book.

Additionally, many readers of *Air Force* have contributed ideas for these cartoons. Space does not permit naming all these individuals—I can only offer as thanks this opportunity to share their humor with more readers through the medium of this book.

However, special thanks must be given to certain individuals and organizations who have aided above and beyond. My deepest gratitude is extended to Capt. Bob Howard, USAF Ret., the Confederate Air Force, and Major Ben Donahue, USAF Ret., for their contributions of humor and encouragement.

Foreword

A LOOK THROUGH ALMOST ANY REFERENCE BOOK can tell you the wingspan of a P-51 or how tall an Atlas missile stood. These are vital facts, to be sure, but these cold hard bits of data don't tell the whole story.

The truth is that people—pilots, maintainers, and even the paper shufflers whose efforts sometimes annoy the pilots and maintainers—are the core of the flying business. Anytime you throw human beings into an equation, there is ample opportunity for humor.

For more than a quarter of a century, Bob Stevens has given us cartoons that have taken note of the parade that is aviation. The drawings have an air of authenticity about them because he really was there—first as a fighter pilot in World War II, and later as a missile squadron commander—but the reason these panels are important doesn't lie in the fact that the rivet rows on an F-86 line up.

Twenty-five years from now, someone wearing an Air Force blue suit on a base on the moon will be able to find out the wingspan of an F-4 from any book, but to find out what it was really like to fly and fix one of those jets, he or she will look to Bob Stevens and his work for *Air Force* magazine.

And that is the true value of Bob Stevens' cartoons. The drawings are an accurate reflection of what life was and is like for those people who have the great fortune to make a living in or around airplanes. And for that, we should all be grateful.

James H. Doolittle, General, USAF Ret.

Introduction

THE DRAWINGS IN THIS BOOK are arranged in a 25-year chronological sequence. Early on in our discussions with the Air Force Association about content, it was decided to include all cartoons published during my tenure. To have been selective might have omitted someone's favorite. So, you get the whole enchilada—the good with the not-so-good. (Frankly, looking back at some of the subject matter, there are some I would like to have omitted!)

The work starts, quite naturally, where I started...sketching for the record while waiting in a "repple depple" during World War II. The reader will note the transition into the jet age, which occurred to me in 1949. Korea jerked us back into combat with war-weary pilots and planes. There's an increasing awareness about this almost forgotten war and I hammered on it, especially in the latter part of the book.

Missiles and silo-sitters get short shrift, I'm sorry to say. This is unexplainable because I was in the first Atlas ICBM squadron to become operational. This lack of coverage can be attributed to the fact that SAC hauled me off to headquarters early on and staff work just isn't my bag. Additionally, there is something so...so inanimate about a huge, cold missile buried deep in a concrete tomb.

Finally, Vietnam—that national hemorrhage—runs on throughout this record because, in time, it spans nearly 50 percent of the entire book. It's hard to find anything funny about 'Nam, but time has mercifully dulled many of the painful edges and enables us to look back at some of the lighter times. Humor is, and always will be, an integral part of military life, just like early morning takeoffs, interminable missions, hours and hours of waiting, long chow lines, lousy weather, drafty tents, dehydrated food, and dysentery.

The men who inspired these cartoons told it like it was. You can accept or ignore the cartoons, but you can't ignore the conditions that produced them.

Bob Stevens

Beginning a new series in AIR FORCE, dedicated to all those aging warriors who bombed from around 18,000 feet or who flew fighters with honest-to-goodness props on 'em or who sweated it out on one island after another or in North Africa or the ETO or you-name-it.

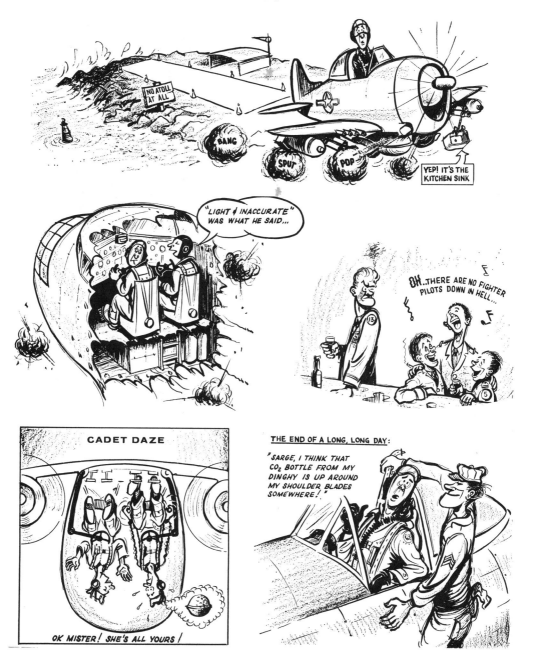

Here's the second in our new AIR FORCE cartoon feature "There I Was..."- the pen and ink brainchild of SAC Lt. Col. Robert M. Stevens, who's reliving Air Force yesteryear for all who had a piece of the action two decades ago (yes, it's that long). This month Bob recreates the mood of how it was when you faced up to your personal role in airpower...for the first, terrifying time...

This page is dedicated to the grease monkeys of the AAF — those skilled technicians who were carefully taught always to use the right tool and the proper part. But the war never seemed to wait for those luxuries to catch up.

The younger Air Force element in South Vietnam today may not be aware that U.S. airmen of an earlier day were also smitten with the infectious charm of Southeast Asia. Here are vignettes of the wartime CBI and Western Pacific...

In the missile age, it turns out, you don't have to be in the least airborne to develop buttocks bunions or alert addle. Today's missileman is indeed heir to all the ills, on and in the ground, that plagued yesterday's crushcaps. And there are those who have suffered then and now.

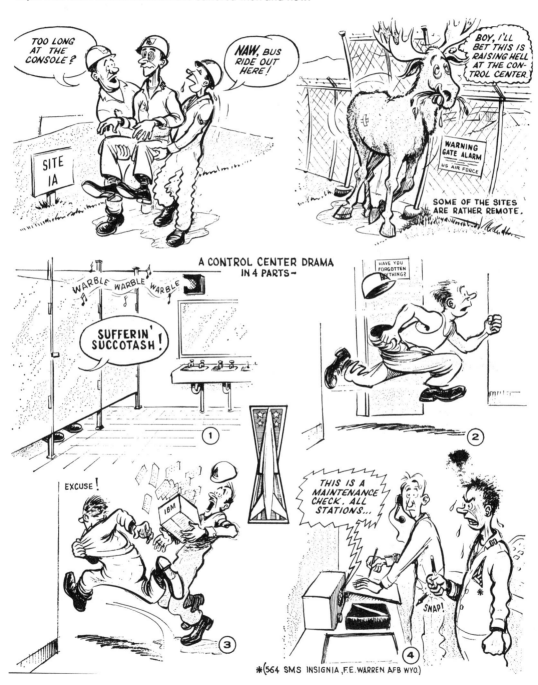

Back in *those* days, when navaids and other essential equipment faltered, the cockpit could prove downright confining. In predicaments like these, it sometimes took a mighty broad sense of humor to carry the day...

Breathes there a bombardier who hasn't at least *almost* pulled this stunt. Back in the days when B-24's were in vogue (and the CBI), the communiques told the folks back home how well our boys were doing the world over. Perhaps it's as well they didn't go into too much detail...

July, 1964 7

What makes it so strange in retrospect is that it really was that way. And the way that it was, wasn't at all the way they told you it would be before you got there. It's a good thing there wasn't too much time to think about it at the time.

Now it can be told...the stirring saga of meticulous airmanship that so well served the Allied cause during World War II. Above all, let us recall those skilled and painstakingly trained pilots who poured forth into combat from training fields across our land.

PILOT TYPES

GUNG-HO WARRIOR

EXECUTIVE TYPE

THE BUZZER

THE RATRACER: "EH-EH-EH-EH, I GOTCHA!"

THE UNCONSCIOUS

THE SURVIVOR

Bob Stevens, the "There-I-Was" man, has just retired from SAC. On his way to vacation in Europe, he stopped off in Washington to do the AFA Convention. After four days of skulking about the Sheraton-Park Hotel with sketchbook and pen, he came up with these impressions...

at the AFA CONVENTION
Sept. 9-12, 1964 • WASHINGTON, D. C.

THERE WERE TOUCHING REUNIONS...

STIMULATING BUSINESS SESSIONS...

(AND, HOO BOY! THOSE EARLY A.M. WORKSHOPS!)

OLD BATTLES WERE REFOUGHT...

There you were — clean-cut, true-blue, an intrepid copilot. Under the direction, of course, of the pilot. You wanted to fly that bird. So what happened? Nothing! Might as well have been in the Quartermaster Corps for all the chance the old buzzard gave you to take the wheel...

THE COPILOT

Looking back, you get that *I wouldn't go through it again for a million bucks but it was a great experience* feeling. But when you were ready for rotation there was one primary emotion...with maybe a twinge of nostalgia for the old air mattress and a condescending regard for your replacement.

"I tell you -- it was hell on the home front! I was so scrogged up by the end of my delay en route to the ZI that it was a pleasure to get back to the combat theater. In fact, when I arrived in England I put out a service star for my mother back in Poughkeepsie..." so goes a World War II ditty about a pilot on leave in the United States.

Stateside duty was sometimes hard to take...when you'd already done an overseas tour. It was training, training and more training. Of course, there were occasional forays into the nearby villages to fraternize with the friendly natives.

The unbounded glee of acceptance as a cadet... arrival of the flight at the flight training center... humiliation at the hands of those infallible upperclassmen... and finally, that indescribable moment of your first solo. Training planes were very cleverly designed with a one-way communication system — to cadet. This made for lots of one-sided conversations.

It has been said that the business of flying can best be described as hours and hours of boredom — interspersed with moments of stark terror. Here are some of the moments of stark terror that have occurred to me in 25 years of flying.

Random Moments of Terror

THE DROPPED FLASHLIGHT BIT:

THE "WHAT-THE-HELL-IS-THAT-HORN?" DRAMA:

THE "NEAR MISS" EXPERIENCE:

Breathes there a pilot whose heart hath ne'er turned flip-flops over some untoward occurrence during the swift completion of his appointed rounds? My CO and I lost a fan on the B-25 one day right after take off — this prompted the following sequence.

THE ENGINE-FAILURE TRAUMA:

QUICK! FEATHER NO.1 WE'VE BLOWN A JUG!

BLAM!
BONK!

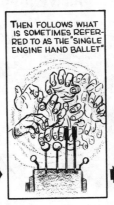

THEN FOLLOWS WHAT IS SOMETIMES REFERRED TO AS THE "SINGLE ENGINE HAND BALLET"

GUESS WHICH ONE YOU FEATHERED AL, GUESS!!

THE "I-DIDN'T-KNOW-IT-WAS-BELOW-MINIMUMS" APPROACH:

CRIPES! WHAT LOUSY WEATHER! THE BIRDS MUST BE WALKIN! THERE'S SOMETHING AHEAD -- MUST BE THE RUNWAY!

①

NOW, TELL ME AGAIN - WHAT WAS THE FIRST THING YOU SAW? ...

②

SEARS

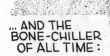

... AND THE BONE-CHILLER OF ALL TIME:

Bandits! 6 o'clock high!

The Navy had their Dilbert; the RAF, Pilot Officer Prune; and the USAAF needed a pilot stereotype. Roger Rudder was the answer. His name came from a bawdy recording made in San Francisco by a wild bunch of fighter pilots headed for R and R stateside.

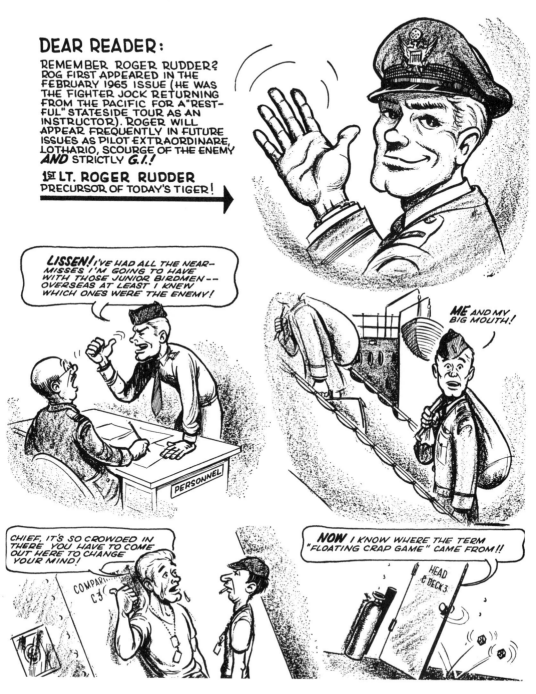

During the second unpleasantness, the lucky ones flew over the big ponds, but the majority of the troops bound for exotic overseas stations sweated it out at eight to eighteen knots aboard one of Uncle's luxury liners.

PORTRAIT OF A GI SHAVING WITH COLD SALT WATER (IT'S LATHER-PROOF)

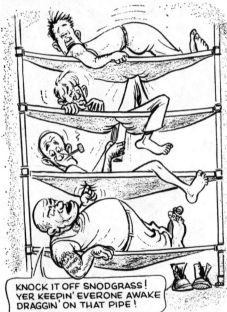

KNOCK IT OFF SNODGRASS! YER KEEPIN' EVERONE AWAKE DRAGGIN' ON THAT PIPE!

ROGER RUDDER

IT SAYS THIS HERE GRAND SALOON HAS A CAPACITY OF 450 PEOPLE...

GENERAL REACTION TO GENERAL QUARTERS.

To paraphrase a Churchillian saying, never was so little
known by so many about so much... but we learned, luv,
we learned. Oh, how we learned!

𝕰𝖓𝖌𝖑𝖆𝖓𝖉, circa 1943, we had an L-of-a lot of experiences:

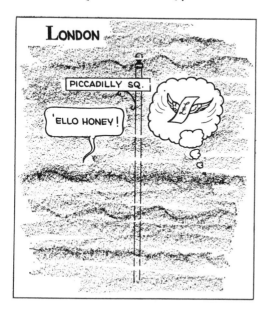

Bouncing along over Europe in a late model B-17 Flying Fort or a B-24 Liberator on air highways paved with flak while friendly and bogie fighters played tag through the formations led one to wonder if the trip was really necessary.

THE AIR OVER EUROPE COULD GET PRETTY CLUTTERED AT TIMES:

THE "GATHERING OF THE CLAN" AT A TYPICAL BRITISH BUNCHER BEACON.

THE UNSEEN AUDIENCE –

We tried to keep soul and sinew together in a military manner, but all those different types you find in an army unnerved us with their separate styles which were unique and sometimes insane. But somehow we managed — somehow.

SCENES WE'D LIKE TO FORGET:

PARACHUTE PACKING DEPT.

THE TIME HACK BOOB

HOW'S THAT AGAIN?

THOSE RUDDY FRENCHMEN FIND THEIR WAY OVER FRANCE BY RECOGNIZING THEIR OWN CHICKENS!!

*ALLIED EXPEDITIONARY AIR FORCE (FREE FRENCH)

ROGER RUDDER

IF IT'S 20 DEGREES BELOW ZERO, HOW COME I'M SWEATING LIKE A HORSE?

Reuniting the old boys and their World War II buddies at Dallas ought to be a touching experience. The new-fangled jet jockeys may snicker, but middle-age spreads or no, the vets of the "old air force" can still hold their own ...

... LOOKING FORWARD TO THE AIR FORCE ASSOCIATION'S 20TH ANNIVERSARY NATIONAL CONVENTION !! DALLAS-FT. WORTH, TEXAS · MAR 22-25 ......Y'ALL COME!

Even as far back as the latter days of World War II, the jet age, with a little age of automation thrown in, was beginning to force itself on the good old "seat of the pants" hotshots. The effect was bewildering. Some still haven't got over it.

THERE ARE A FEW GUYS AROUND WHO'LL REMEMBER – WITH CONSIDERABLE TRAUMA – WHEN THE JERRIES USHERED IN THE JET & ROCKET ERA:

Fighter jocks were always telling the bomber crews what a soft deal bomber duty was — just sitting there driving in a straight line with all those engines, with all those guns, with all those fighters to protect you. But as any bomber man will tell you, it wasn't all that easy.

The crew chief's idea of heaven must be the Air Force Museum where airplanes are polished to perfection and never flown again. But then, what else could match the pride he felt in pasting another meatball or swastika on the cockpit of his personal instrument of war, which was occasionally loaned out to some thoughtless pilot.

In the wartime milieu, the thinking man had frequent cause for serious reflection upon the vicissitudes of his lot, in which one's foresight and careful attention to detail often resulted in complete disaster...

THE NERVOUS SENTRY

SOURCE UNKNOWN

Decisions were always difficult in war time. There were times when you didn't know what to do and many, many more times when nothing you did was right.

Nothing, but virtually nothing, was like what they taught us at our stateside training fields once we got exposed to the realities of the combat zone. But there was a certain satisfaction in knowing that no one else seemed to have the poop either.

AH! THOSE ENGLISH MORNS!

RED LEADER, HOW'S THE VISIBILITY? CAN YOU SEE THE LIGHTS?

SEE THE *LIGHTS!* HELL, I CAN'T EVEN SEE MY COPILOT!

HEY MAC, WHERE'S THE LATRINE?

YER STANDIN' IN IT, JACK!

(MAN, OH MAN! THOSE BLACKOUTS)

SURE WAY TO WIN A POPULAR-ITY POLL IN A DEBRIEFING --

AND SO ON ACROSS EUROPE

BREAK LEFT!

OOPS! I MEAN BLINDMAN FLIGHT-'BREAK LEFT'

WE HAD A LOT TO LEARN ABOUT INSTRUMENT FLYING —

HEY BLINDMAN LEADER! YOU HAPPEN TO NOTICE WHICH WAY OUR TIP TANKS WENT?

Of course, the USO came out our way whenever they could. But for the most part, in these tropic climates, we created our own diversions and through it all there was that ever present spirit of camaraderie marred only occasionally by little spurts of hysteria.

THE LONG OVERWATER FERRY MISSION –

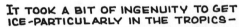

In his dispensary tent the doc could be heartless when all you wanted was a little extra sack time or a dash of medicinal spirits. But when he ventured out of his office into yours, he occasionally revealed more human tendencies.

THE DOC WHO HEARD THE BOYS WERE GOING TO HAVE A "DANCE" SATURDAY NIGHT—

SOMETIMES IT JUST *SEEMED* LIKE THIS—

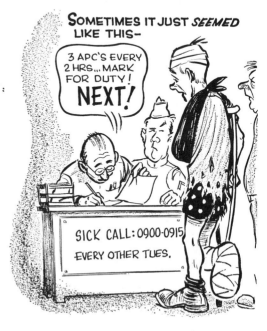

MOST FLIGHT SURGEONS, GOD BLESS 'EM, FLEW WITH THE TROOPS OCCASIONALLY—

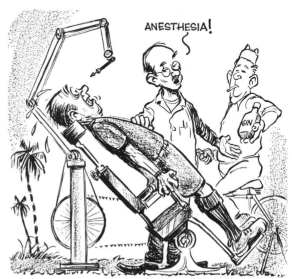

EQUIPMENT AND SUPPLIES WERE LIMITED IN SOME AREAS—

The legendary Earl B. "Earthquake Magoon" McGovern, a one-time wing-man of mine, made the landing shown here at Mitchell Air Force Base one winter. After World War II, "Earthquake" became a soldier of fortune in China and "bought the farm" in a C-119 at Dien Bien Phu.

Were any of us really satisfied with things as they were? Of course not! By applying a little effort we could invariably make them worse.

THE STORM FRONT PENETRATION—

Back in the days when an airplane without a propeller was treated with suspicion and awe, one Lieutenant "Dusty" Rhoades (all Rhoades in the air force are "Dusty"), a jet fighter instructor at Nellis Air Force Base, created a legend when he made an unscheduled RON at a SAC base.

Pilots, especially the Air Force type, have always been considered a special breed, with their own eccentricities, their own way of doing things and their own brand of stubbornness.

A CONTROL TOWER DRAMA IN 3 PARTS

TOWER, THIS IS AIR FORCE 2345. I ONLY HAVE **5 GALLONS** OF FUEL LEFT! RE-QUEST INSTRUCTIONS. *OVER!*

TOWER TO 2345 *!* DON'T PANIC *!!* -- **STAY CALM!** WHAT IS YOUR *EXACT* LOCATION... *OVER!*

CRASH ALARM

AFTER A LONG PAUSE -

I'M PARKED ON THE RAMP. I WAS WONDER-ING WHERE THE FUEL TRUCK WAS...

PILOT PORTRAITS

THE COPILOT WHO'S JUST SEEN THE PILOT TAKE HIS ST. CHRISTOPHER MEDAL OFF THE INSTRUMENT PANEL & PUT IT IN HIS POCKET...

FAMOUS LAST WORDS

ABORT? **NEGATIVE!** *She'll smooth out!*

Airmen are a sterling lot, well and rightly known for their intrepid spirit. But on a few rare occasions, for what they considered good and sufficient cause, they may turn just a little bit crooked.

Scene: A Link trainer in cadet training —

San Francisco! City of cable cars, spectacular sights, superb restaurants, uninhibited night life, and meeting place for this year's AFA Convention! "San Fran" took the AFAers to its heart and vice versa. For four days the Air Force held the city in siege ... and when it was over the natives were just as glad ...

At the AFA Convention
San Francisco — March 14-17

NO SURVIVOR WILL EVER FORGET HOW THE TROOPS — AND THEIR GALS — COMMANDEERED THE CABLE CARS (EVEN THE FAKE ONES ON TRUCK CHASSIS USED TO TRANSPORT AFA ers TO & FROM SOCIAL EVENTS). MAN! YOU HAVEN'T LIVED UNTIL YOU'VE BAILED OUT OF TWO PRANGED CABLE CARS IN ONE EVENING!!

NAVIGATOR TO PILOT!

CLANG! CLANG!

POP THE DRAG CHUTE!

MY INSURANCE — DID I PAY MY INSURANCE?

POWELL & MARKET 504

THERE WERE NOTABLES EVERYWHERE YOU LOOKED... HERE'S JUST A FEW — —

THAT'S A SHAU — NOT AW SHAW!

"BERNIE" FISHER — AF'S NEWEST MEDAL OF HONOR WINNER

COL. "GABBY" GABRESKI — STILL OUR LEADING ACE (WW II & KOREA).

GEN. LEMAY (RET. COS) WHO'S AS CONCISE WITH A PHRASE AS HE EVER WAS!

'STARS FELL ON CALIFORNIA' — 132 OF 'EM TO BE EXACT — AT THE CHIEF'S LUNCHEON

JESS LARSON — OUTGOING PREXY

HILTON HOTEL

PSSST! WHO'S MINDING THE STORE?

18

19

THE NIGHT FIGHTER'S REUNION WAS A SPECIAL EVENT THAT DREW A BIG TURNOUT. CELEBRITIES, MILITARY AND MUFTI, FILLED THE ROOM... AH YOUTH!

YOU BOB LANSING?

...RECOGNIZED YOUR EYES.

YEP

THAT'S *GOT* TO BE GEN. THATCHER!

L. MENDEL RIVERS, THAT FIGHTIN' CONGRESSMAN FROM SO. CAROLINA →

REMEMBER BOYS, CONGRESS IS ONE OF YOUR ALLIES!!

TYPICAL SCENE OF A "CONTINENTAL" BREAKFAST... AT **7 AM**, YET!

THERE OUGHT TO BE A BETTER WAY TO START THE DAY THAN BY GETTING UP!

TO WIND IT UP -- TENNESSEE ERNIE FORD M.C.'D THE GREAT HONORS NIGHT SHOW AS ONLY OL' ERN CAN DO IT! THE AIR FORCE PAID SPECIAL TRIBUTE TO- AMONG OTHERS-THE AIR RESCUE UNITS IN VIETNAM...KNOWN ESPECIALLY AS **THE JOLLY GREEN GIANTS!**

WELL! BLESS YOUR PEA-PICKIN' HEART!

In the old timer's air war in Europe, it was noisy, crowded and often very hot. Conditions which, except for the high metal content of the atmosphere, their colleagues on the Aleutian chain would have welcomed.

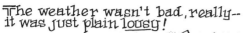

Wars are won, they say, by the side that makes fewer mistakes. Obviously our valiant air leaders succeeded in forging a sharply-honed, well-oiled, high-gear fighting machine able to rise above the drolleries perpetrated by the chowderheads in our midst. The sequence involving the control tower is probably the oldest saw in aviation.

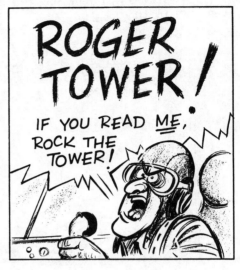

SITUATION: YOU'VE BEEN TRYING TO 'RAISE' THE TOWER FOR OVER 5 MINUTES. OBVIOUSLY YOU'RE 'PUTTING OUT', BUT THE TOWER WON'T ANSWER --- *FINALLY:*

AIR FORCE AIRCRAFT CIRCLING THE FIELD, IF YOU READ THE TOWER - ROCK YOUR WINGS!!

ROGER TOWER!
IF YOU READ ME, ROCK THE TOWER!

COULD I GIVE YOU ANOTHER ONE, COL.? I'M ON O.J.T.

ROGER RUDDER:

OKAY, OKAY! WHO'S THE JOKER COMPLAININ' ABOUT TOO MANY G's?

LT. RUDDER, PLEEZE!

OPERAT
460TH FI
A
FLT. LDR.
RUDDER
JONES
SMITH
JAME

Nothing much has changed in twenty-five years. Looking back, we seemed little better than boors when we sought to confound with facts those of our brethren who had already made up their minds.

Scene: A USAAF training base: 1942

AIR CORPS 567, MAKE A 360 OVER KELLY BEACON AND LOSE ONE MINUTE IN SPACING, GO AHEAD—

KELLY TOWER, THIS IS 567, FOR YOUR INFORMATION IT TAKES **TWO** MINUTES TO MAKE A 360!

ROGER 567, THEN MAKE A 180 AND **BACK IN!**

Famous last words:

① QUIT SWEATING THOSE *6! FUEL GAUGES!! WE'VE GOT A COUPLE HUNDRED WHEN THEY SHOW "EMPTY."

②

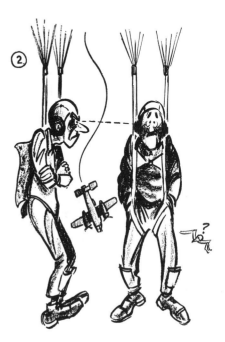

Everyone is convinced there is all the time in the world to conduct a war — then for some strange reason the enemy suddenly begins to take you seriously.

REMEMBER THE OLD SAYING, "THERE'S SAFETY IN NUMBERS"?

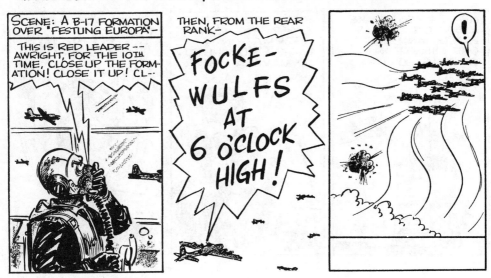

CONTROL TOWERS SEEMED SO FAR REMOVED FROM THE PROBLEM—

Here is a fond look back at some of the everyday occurrences and annoyances that made life in the service during the Big War such a truly unforgettable experience.

Better it were that the young gentlemen of the Air Force Academy and sundry aircrew training institutions be kept uninformed on the aberrant behavior of their predecessors. Though aging colleagues recall them with nought but the fondest memories, precise professionals in today's air arm would undoubtedly classify them as yesterday's hippies...

Beauty, they say is in the eye of the beholder. That plane you flew may have been only a bucket of bolts, but the mental pictures it evoked in those beholden to it could really turn out to be beauts.

That magnificent WW II flying machine of yours — as seen by:

The manufacturer—
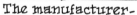

Your crew chief—

The Flying Safety Officer—

Supply—

Armament—

Communications—

Your wife—

... and you—

Everybody has his problems and foibles in the mad, mad business of pushing yourself through the air from one point to another. But every once in a while you meet somebody of whom it must be said, "There's one in every crowd".

TWO TRUE TALES:

Scene: CBI; A gaggle of "Jugs" (P-47's) on a long, LONG range mission We look at Red 2--

GEEZ, SOLID UNDERCAST, TARGET'S COMIN' UP-- FUEL'S LOW, TOO.

RED LEADER THIS IS RED 2 BINGO*!

*CODE FOR MINIMUM FUEL FOR RETURN TO HOME BASE.

OKAY RED 2 THIS IS RED LEADER, YOU STICK WITH ME- I GOT LOTS!

TALE 2

Scene: A MATS bird way out over the big pond. An overeager check pilot is "giving them hell"

FEATHERING

HEH, HEH I'LL FEATHER #3

FLIGHT ENGINEER

FEATHERING

PUNCH!

OKAY SIR, IT'S YOUR TURN AGAIN!

Well, we did learn how to fly and even to land, but what was sad was that we rarely had a chance to take along as passengers those sadistic creatures who tortured us in the Link Trainers. Their hearts were colder than the metal and glass of the instruments we finally came to understand and sometimes even to believe.

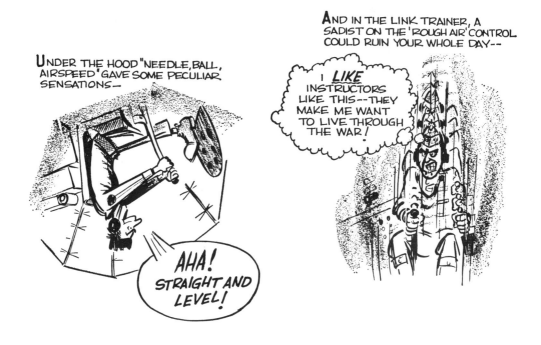

It's never been much of a treat to bail out of an airplane, but I have to admit that there's been considerable progress in the art of retrieval since the days when a raft was where you stood a good chance of spending the rest of the war.

WWII FIGHTER PILOT SURVIVAL GEAR (S.W. PACIFIC)

IF YOU SURVIVED THE CHUTE OPENING SHOCK, A CONVERTED B17 ('DUMBO') MIGHT DROP A WHOLE LIFE BOAT ON YOU --

TODAY IN VIETNAM, TECHNOLOGY HAS MADE RESCUE ALMOST ROUTINE --- ALMOST

It used to be a pretty easy business to get off the ground. But those days are gone forever. Now, with planes big enough to carry Barnum & Bailey's whole circus and with all that air traffic, you might just as well be driving the old Chevy and fighting the freeways.

As we've noted on the preceding pages several times, nothing — well, hardly anything — seemed to work out in the crisp and correct manner outlined in the book. It made you wonder if maybe you'd have been better off in the infantry.

P.S. IT'S HAPPENED TO MANY A GOOD MAN—

REMEMBER THE GOOD OLD TRAINING DAYS WHEN THE INSTRUCTOR HELD THE FUNNEL END OF THE GOSPORT OUT IN THE SLIPSTREAM TO GET YOUR ATTENTION?

FUN, EH?

IF YOU DON'T THINK WE WERE A 'MIXED BAG', OBSERVE THIS U.S. PILOT, BASED IN ITALY, FLYING AN ENGLISH 'MOSQUITO ABOUT TO BUZZ OFF ON TDY FROM FRANCE TO BRITAIN —

O/S STRIPES—
(LOOK LIKE RANK OF FRENCH CAPT.)

RAF WINGS

U.S. WINGS

'IKE' JACKET

PINKS

RAF BOOTS

The invasion of "Fortress Europe" by the greatest armada of aircraft ever assembled was launched on D-Day, June 6, 1944. Gliders, transports, bombers and fighters all rode shotgun for the great movement across the Channel. All in all, it was quite a show.

JUNE 6, 1944

Can it already be twenty years since USAF's first big pilot reconversion program when Mustang and Thunderbolt jocks joined their two- and four-engined brethren in flying the big, fat, slow birds on the tightrope to Berlin? They did a lasting job.

JUNE 26, 1948, 'CALLUP DAY' CAUGHT MANY CREWS IN VARIOUS STATES OF READINESS —

WELL SIR, Y'SEE WE WERE ON THE 3RD TEE AT HICKAM AND...

RHEIN MAIN

THE WEATHER? LET'S HEAR HOW IT WAS IN GERMANY FROM AN OLD EXPERT —

IT WAS LOUSY, JUST PLAIN *LOUSY!*

HAULING COAL HAD ITS LIGHTER SIDE —

YOU GIVE ME THAT 'COAL DUST TWINS' ONE MORE TIME...AN' *POW!*

LE MAY'S COAL & FEED CO.

THE GROUND CREWS, BLESS 'EM, WORKED AROUND THE CLOCK. THOSE UNLOADING CARGOS LOOKED LIKE THIS —

HEY FELLAS! I'M A WALKIN' CASSEROLE!

CEREAL   MACARONI

FLOUR   BEANS   POTATOES   XXX

SOMETHING *HAD* TO BREAK THE MONOTONY — AND, AS USUAL, IT WAS GI-INSPIRED SONGS AND DITTIES

TEN TONS TO TEMPELHOF

FULDA RADIO, THIS IS 'SMALL CHANGE ON THE RANGE'

OR (YUK, YUK) 4 NICKELS OVER FULDA

BIG WILLIE, HERE'S OL' 77 WITH A LOAD OF COAL FOR OUR DAILY GOAL!

TALK ABOUT FAST TURN-AROUND TIMES! GANDER AT THE BRIEFING TEAM AT WORK IN A C-54 AT 'BIG B'

HERE'S YOUR WEATHER-READY TO COPY?

LATRINE PILOTS ONLY

ROGER

AND THERE WERE THOSE BIERSTUBE LOTHARIOS—

I CONCERN MYSELF WITH FLOUR & POTATOES— ALTHOUGH I'M NOT ABOVE HAULING MACARONI

WEARY? MAN, THOSE EARLY DAYS WERE *TOUGH* ON A GUY!

LE'SEE, 4 BAGS — I MUST'VE BEEN HERE 4 WEEKS NOW.

FLY SAFE

IT ALL SEEMED WORTH IT WHEN SOME SCRAWNY GERMAN KID OFFER-ED HIS OR HER MOST PRIZED POSSESS-ION TO YOU IN GRATITUDE ~

If you can remember Jackie Coogan, you may also recall the Army Air Force's glider fleets that delivered airborne troops in the Burmese jungles as well as behind the Normandy beaches on D-Day. Who's Coogan? Before becoming a U.S.A.A.F. glider pilot, he once played "The Kid" opposite Charlie Chaplin. Now, who's Chaplin?

THOSE 'BAMBOO BOMBERS' — THE GLIDERS — AS SEEN BY:

— THE TOW SHIP CREW

— GLIDER PILOTS THEMSELVES

— THE AIRBORNE TROOPS

— SECOND & THIRD WAVE GLIDER PILOTS

— GERMAN GUNNERS

— AND FINALLY, AS SEEN BY THE OCCUPIED COUNTRIES ON D-DAY

The years have brought us lows and highs
And long endurance in the skies;
Solid missiles, the sonic boom...
And the record sheet has lots more room.

AIRMEN'S UNABRIDGED DICTIONARY

BUZZ JOB
(verb) To fly low. "Cut the grass." Final maneuver practiced by many pilots no longer with us.

FLAT HAT (verb)
To stunt, show off, 'grandstand.' Derived from the old AAF custom of leveling the headgear of 'groundpounder' reviewing stand officers (archaic)

GADGET (noun)
Aviation cadet. Usually found in a position of aggravated brace. According to upperclassmen, something lower than a snake's belly.

S.O.S. (acronym)
Polite form - 'slop on a shingle'; describes that mixture of creamed (hah!) chipped beef on toast. Usually served on a morning when you had a queasy stomach anyway.

Aviatrix Jacqueline Cochran banded together a group of women pilots to form the Woman's Auxiliary Service Pilots (WASP). And, brother, some of them could sting like their namesakes. I'll never forget trying to get one to move over on a pilot lounge seat to make room for some other weary pilots. (She was stretched out full length.) She used some very un-teaparty-like language telling me where to go!

After waiting for the weather to clear,
after those days of checking and rechecking,
after the suspense of the countdown —
nothing could go wrong-wrong-wrong...

Back in the good old days — which is to say in the 1940's and through the '50's — sometimes there were more bad days than good. But now, in today's modern, streamlined, jet-propelled, worldwide air service, things are different. Aren't they?

Here's the second entry in Bob Stevens' new illustrated dictionary for aviation buffs (the first entry appeared in AF/SD for September '68). Send in your favorite old AF term — it might be worth five bucks... (Offer expired March 1969, Ed.)

AIRMEN'S UNABRIDGED DICTIONARY

CLANK UP (verb) State of extreme agitation. Usually brought on by such statements as "overseas, special mission, check ride, the C.O. wants to see you..." etc.

FIREWALL (verb and noun) (1) Act of pulling 65 in. of manifold pressure from an engine designed to give only 50. (2) Section of the aircraft specially designed to allow all engine heat and smoke to fill the cockpit.

FIGMO (acronym) Quaint old Anglo-Saxon expression used by "short-timers" to tell the neophytes what to do. Stands for "_____, I Got My Orders". (no polite form)

GAGGLE (noun) A large number of anything headed in the same general direction in the same part of the sky. Often used to describe a USAAF tight formation.

Everyone had his own heroic ideas on skill and daring, of course, but sometimes it was tempting to see how safe you could play it...

Bob Stevens tips his hard hat to that splendid team at NASA's Manned Spacecraft Center, and to the men they help keep aloft. Consider the GI of Tomorrow. Will his lot be much different in space? Probably not...

HERE'S TO THOSE UNSUNG HEROES OF THE SPACE PROGRAM WHO MAN THE CONSOLES —ON THE DECK.

ONE THING WORSE THAN THE 'NIGHT WATCH' IS MONITORING SPACE CHOW TIME ON THE BOOB TUBE...

IMAGINE! A THREE-DAY PASS FROM A SPACE STATION! ...QUO VADIS?

SOME THINGS, LIKE MORNING REPORTS, WILL ALWAYS BE WITH US

When jets first came on the scene, a new book had to be written. The sequences depicted below were attributed to a 2nd Lt. Bruce Jones. Bruce developed the "Selfridge Let-down" long before anyone ever heard of a "teardrop" jet instrument approach pattern...

The subject is communications — or the lack thereof. Messages half received or misunderstood might just as well have been sent by Pony Express instead of at the speed of light...

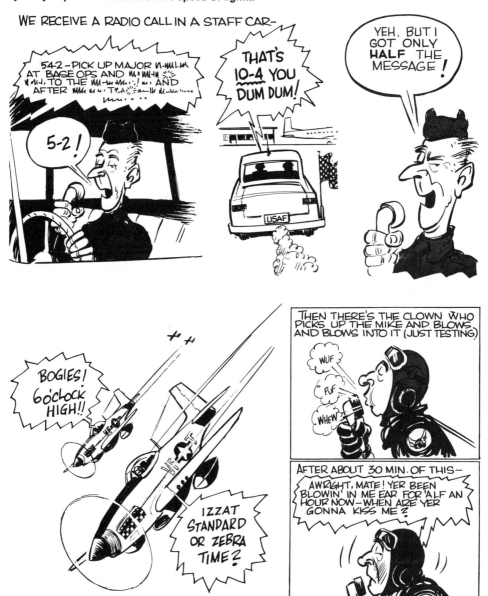

P.S. THERE'S ONE IN EVERY OUTFIT!

In addition to the traditional World War II sayings we include a couple from Vietnam and the missile age. As the old saw goes: "These, too, shall pass".

AIRMEN'S UNABRIDGED DICTIONARY

SCARF UP (skarf up) v., From Vietnam. To grab, rescue, capture, as "scarfed up by the Jolly Green Giants." Unfortunately, can also be used as "scarfed up by the V.C."

CLOOGE (kloogh), n. (Espec. among missile men) Any improvised or makeshift repair, using old tin cans, chewing gum, etc., to simulate first class work in Tech Order compliance. Usual results will not pass close 'eyeball'.

PRANG (prang), v. To damage an aircraft by contact with an immovable object—such as the ground. n. A loud noise accompanying the termination of an aircraft flight; usually preceded by a rapid descent.

'50 MISSION HAT'

RAUNCHY (ronchee), n. Descriptive term usually applied to 2nd Lts., Airmen Basic, and Doolies at the USAF Academy. Contemporary use applies to some college students, most rock-and-roll outfits and all Hippies.

A salute to the magnificent men in their Liberator machines — the stalwarts who, a generation ago, carried the air war to the enemy's doorstep — She was big and she was heavy, but could she ever deliver!

THE MOST IMPORTANT PIECE OF EQUIPMENT IN THE 'LIB' WAS A EMPTY 50 CAL. AMMO BOX --

Where's the *⑥! ⚡☆! ammo box?!

(P.S. IT WENT UNDER HERE — TO KEEP THE NOSE DOWN ON THE GROUND).

CROSS SECTION OF THE BOMBARDIER AND NAVIGATOR WORKING(?) IN THE 24's SPACIOUS NOSE SECTION.

What sadist designed this?

Ball turret to navigator = knock off using that relief tube up there!! - GUB

Here's lookin' up yore address!

LEGEND HAS IT YOU COULD SPOT A B-24 JOCK BY HIS OVER-DEVELOPED LEFT ARM (from horsin' the yoke around)!

THE ULTIMATE INSULT

No kiddin'! Does that thing really fly?

Too Big and Too Heavy!

Some men who drive weapon-laden airplanes with utter nonchalance get a little sweaty-palmed when handed a loaded pistol. Even a flare gun earns a certain respect. On the other hand, the darn thing might not have even been loaded...

Now that the majority of us winged warriors of World War II are sprouting gray hairs among the gold, this meander down memory lane may serve to help conjure up those splendid days of our bygone youth...

REMEMBER?

•Those 'PARACHUTE BAGS' LOADED WITH EVERYTHING BUT A PARACHUTE YOU TOOK WITH YOU PCS, TDY TDN, ETC., ETC.

... AND THOSE SHEEP-SKIN FLYING DUDS, (USUALLY ISSUED IN THE TROPICS)

KASPRONG! (SOUND OF A HERNIA)

•THAT GREAT WARTIME BOOZE MADE OF '100% NATURAL **CANE** SPIRITS'?

OLD PANTHER POOP

THIS STUFF'D BLOW A SAFE!

•TRYING TO HIT THE JOHN IN THE BACK OF A GOONEY-BIRD IN ROUGH AIR?

•TROPICAL 'BUTTER' THAT REFUSED TO MELT? (IT JUST SHRIVELLED UP AND TURNED BLACK!)

SPUT

•HAVING 84 POINTS IN AN AREA WITH 85 POINTS FOR ROTATION ??

•THE 'RUPTURED DUCK' LAPEL PIN?

Men and machines sometimes show startling similarities. There are days when it's easy to get up and get going, but there are other days when the only thing that works is a boot on the backside...

Whether apprehensive or devil-may-care, any warrior on duty in the darkness of night might well appreciate these words from Shakespeare's King Lear: "Things that love night / love not such nights as these. The wrathful skies / Gallow the very wanderers of the dark / And make them keep their caves."

A SENTRY POST ON A FLIGHT LINE IN WW II –

* sound of a rifle bolt sliding home

THIS HAS GOT TO BE ONE OF THE HOARIEST LEGENDS IN THE AIR FORCE. SITUATION: TWO CADETS ON A NIGHT CROSS COUNTRY

The story is true. Only the names have been omitted - to protect the magazine from lawsuit. I won't say who the star of the show was -- all I'll admit to is, "There I was…"

Instructors who live and keep their sanity
Are often lacking in urbanity.
The student — duller than a hoe —
is the guy who makes it so...

SCENE: INSTRUMENT FLIGHT CHECK WITH A PARTICULARLY SNOTTY INSTRUCTOR-

AWRIGHT MISTER! CORRECT 2° LEFT *NOW!*

2° IN THIS ROUGH AIR?!

OKAY, THEN MAKE IT 10° LEFT AND 8° TO THE RIGHT!

BLIND FLYING HOOD
KNUCKLES, WHITE

SCENE: A PRIMARY JET TRAINING BASE; A DUAL RIDE, INSTRUCTOR TO NEW T-37* STUDENT TAXIING OUT FOR TAKEOFF:

*AFFECTIONATELY CALLED THE 'TWEETY-BIRD' OR 'CONVERTER' (CONVERTS FUEL INTO NOISE)

OKAY, LET'S GO TO 100% NOW.

NO! NO! NOT THE THROTTLE

ROAR

←(REACHING FOR OXYGEN REGULATOR)

The good, the bad, the droll, the sad
Add up to war's perdition.
For airmen, long-of-tooth or young,
They're part of the tradition...

Remember **GREMLINS?** Inherited from the RAF (1928). There were good ones, bad ones, mischievous ones — they all had one thing in common: "They were the little men who usually were not there"—

(THE LANDING GEAR THAT WASN'T)

Another ubiquitous group during WW II (and in Korea and Vietnam, too!) was the U.S.O.- God bless 'em!

And will you ever forget *these* characters?...

KILROY

thanks to Sgt. Geo. Baker

in memory of Lt. Dave Breger

"The time has come," the artist said,
"To speak of many things...
the ups and downs of flying clowns,
And cannons wearing wings."

ROGER RUDDER

- PILOT EXTRAORDINAIRE
- BON VIVANT!
- ALL-ROUND GOOD FELLOW
- _and_ EXPENDABLE!
(BEING A SECOND LOOEY)

ROG IS DEMONSTRATING A SLOW ROLL TO A CADET

: * ⊙ ! * !₵
Fell out of it! Boy! am I ever screwed up!
* ⊙ !
←OVER R/T _NOT_ INTERCOM

-- AND FROM THE TOWER-

Aircraft that just made a transmission! Give the tower your call sign!!

LISSEN BUSTER, I'M NOT _THAT_ SCREWED UP!!!

GENERAL GEORGE KENNEY'S WARRIORS IN 5TH AIR FORCE RIGGED UP A **75 MM** CANNON IN A B-25....IT WAS A REAL RIVET POPPER! ACTUALLY IT COULD FIRE QUITE RAPIDLY AND MADE ONE HELLOFA STRAFING WEAPON!!

Man! that's what I call recoil!!

BARROOM!

NORTH AMERICAN BUILT MORE THAN 1400 OF THESE BIRDS (the 'G' & 'H')

POOR ROBERT'S 'ALMANAK'

FEB 1905 CAPT. THOS. BALDWIN IN HIS AIRSHIP 'CALIFORNIA ARROW' RACES AN AUTOMOBILE 10 MILES (L.A. TO PASADENA, CALIF.) -- AND WINS BY 3 MIN.!

Yeh! but I hit 4 stop lights in Los Angeles!

JUNE 1908 AIR STRENGTH OF THE U.S. ARMY IS 3 OFFICERS AND 10 MEN – ALL IN ONE BASKET!

U.S. BALLOON CORPS

Sleep well, America! Your Air Force is awake tonight!

JULY 1909 FINAL TEST FLIGHT OF THE FIRST GOVT. AIRCRAFT.

Now dive it to terminal velocity!

GASP 60 MPH?

OCT 1918 AIR PASSENGER SERVICE BETWEEN KEY WEST, FLA., AND CUBA INAUGURATED.

An' it's still operating! (off and on)

JUNE 1927 CHAMBERLAIN AND LEVINE FLY NONSTOP FROM N.Y. TO GERMANY - 3905 MI. - IN 42 HRS; THEIR SHIP - 'COLUMBIA'!

Can you beat that?

Columbia

P.S. This one made it from the moon to earth in 60 hrs!

JAN 1929 MAJ. SPAATZ AND CAPT. EAKER, PLUS CREW OF 3, SET REFUELING ENDURANCE RECORD OF 150 HRS 40 MIN. OVER L.A.

Regular or ethyl? *

* And that's where that old saw came from!

Retractable landing gear added a new dimension to flying — more speed, more maneuverability, more things to forget. When they first appeared, belly landings were as common as that ol' Air Force saying, "I couldn't hear the tower because of that horn blowin' in my ear!"

While all airmen perforce belong to that elite brotherhood of the noble, a heroic stance is difficult to maintain once the winds of adversity begin to blow, and you find yourself shot down in flames — or in conversation...

THE SQUADRON HOTSHOT (EVERY OUTFIT'S GOT AT LEAST ONE) IS MOUTHING OFF-

INSTRUMENT INSTRUCTORS COULD BE PARTICULARLY SARCASTIC—

Back in the days when not all airmen were all-airmen, riding shotgun in a C-45 could be a good way to catch up on your sleep. But sometimes it called for ambassadorial self control...

We trained and we trained and we trained, and we knew the gadgets and gimmicks cold. Or that's what we thought when we got our wings. But somehow, in the cold reality of flight, not everything came up roses...

Here's to the chaplains, God bless 'em. The best of them spent a lot of time on the line and in the air. They knew when to talk, when to listen... and when not to listen...

SCENE: AN AAF CONTROL TOWER c. 1943. A NEW PILOT IS CHECKING OUT.

HI PADRE! WHATCHA DOIN' UP HERE? EXPECTING THE WORST?

NO I COME UP FOR INSPIRATION

HERE HE COMES! LET'S...

SHHH! CPL. LET'S LISTEN..

A L-O-N-G PAUSE, THEN—

OKAY GOD, I'LL TAKE IT NOW!

THEN THERE'S THE 'SKY PILOT' WHO WAS RIDING RIGHT SEAT IN A C-45

NICE LANDING.

THANKS, CHAPLAIN

KERUNCH

THE GEAR LEVER!

FEEL FREE TO SAY SOMETHING APPROPRIATE, LIEUTENANT.

It was 1944, and our magnificent men and their flying machines were locked in a gargantuan struggle to restore peace to a world in flames. But even in the midst of the holocaust, it was the minor problems dealt with every day that kept things interesting.

The tributaries feeding into the generation gap are the terminology chasm and the credibility canyon. In any case, old and bold flyers are certain to recognized old and bold liars...

ROGER RUDDER

Flexible planning is a virtue often practiced in inverse ratio to one's distance from the problem. But how marvelously the mind concentrates on alternatives when the planner's own anatomy is in the well-known sling!

The Air Force Association was born on this month in 1946. The AAF nearly died. There had been a mass exodus of WW II-weary troops and those remaining had to pull double — and <u>triple</u> duty.

IN 1946, WHEN AFA WAS BORN, THE AAF NEARLY DIED. THERE WAS A MASS EXODUS OF WWII-WEARY TROOPS.

SIGH

COMMANDER
ADJ.
CLERK, COOK
GUARD, ETC.

ONE MIGHT SAY KOREA BROKE IN A HURRY

...AN' TO THINK THE DAY BEFORE YESTERDAY I WAS SELLIN' SHOES IN DOWNTOWN BURBANK!

AND THEN THERE WAS 'NAM':

LESSEE, WHERE WAS THE LAST PLACE WE SERVED TOGETHER?...SAIPAN?... RHEIN-MAIN?... TAEGU...?

PILOT COL. R.

DONG HA

THINGS PICKED UP WITH OUR FIRST JETS —

THERE AIN'T NO SUCH THING!

JONES

SGT JONES PROP SHOP

THE MISSILE AGE WAS MET WITH MIXED EMOTIONS —

USAF

HOT DAWG! NO MORE RETURNING ABORTS!

WELL, THERE GOES THE OL' FLIGHT PAY!

When fighter jocks misread their clocks
And don't fire on the hour,
It gives this dude disquietude—
And super pucker power.

Engines and airframes and armaments change,
As do ceilings and airspeeds and ferry range,
But what keeps 'em flying — according to rumor —
is the airman's kind of wild-blue humor.

'FREDDY THE FAC'

We turn from things with guns and jets and sweptback wings
To some rare old birds, for these "Almanacks" and Airmen's
Dictionaries.

POOR ROBERT'S ALMANACK

DEC 12, 1915

ALL-STEEL "BATTLE PLANE" IS TESTED.

FEB 27, 1920

MAJ. RUDOLPH W. SCHROEDER, IN AN ARMY AIR SERVICE SUPER-CHARGED 'LE PERE' AIRCRAFT, SETS AN ALTITUDE RECORD OF 33,113 FT!

JULY 13, 1929

START OF AIRCRAFT EN-DURANCE FLIGHT OF FORREST O'BRIEN AND DALE JACKSON IN A CURTIS-ROBIN WHICH BREAKS 400-HR MARK.

JUNE 10, 1948

U.S. AIR FORCE ANNOUNCES THAT CHUCK YEAGER EXCEEDED SPEED OF SOUND IN THE X-1 THE PREVIOUS OCTOBER.

If at first you don't succeed, try, try again.
Disregard the small arms:
Thanks to you, whom we admire,
Those cotton-pickin' fighter jocks will fly, fly again.

Many will remember "Operation Crossroads" — the atom bomb tests at Bikini's blue atoll. The public recalls the awesome mushroom clouds. Members of the 58th Wing will never forget the human drama that unfolded.

1946 – TASK FORCE 1.52 IS EN ROUTE TO BIKINI FOR THE A-BOMB TESTS....AH, BIKINI!

CENSORED

– THEN THEY LANDED!

POOF!

NO LOVE ATOLL

THE MAIN TOPIC AT THE CLUB BARS WAS –

WHAT THE BOMB LOOKS LIKE

KWAJALEIN DRESS: PITH HELMET, SHORTS and BOONDOCKERS (PONCHOS WERE ALSO FASHIONABLE!)

ABLE DAY 1 JULY 1946 – WHILE THOUSANDS WATCHED 'DAVE'S DREAM' – A B-29 – DROPPED THE BOMB ON A CAPTIVE TARGET FLEET –

I'M SO NERVOUS.... WHAT IF I MISS? *

* HE DID! – BUT IN A-BOMB DISTANCES, NOT SO FAR YOU'D NOTICE.

Above, god-like, he pirouettes and whirls
As toward the guns, us fighter-jock he hurls.
And this we'd like to do as we attack —
Reach out our hands and choke that bloody FAC!

FAC-TO-FIGHTER-JOCKS —
I HAVEN'T SEEN ANY GROUND FIRE — IT'S A GOOD TARGET. C'MON IN!

12,000 FT.

1000 FT.

*%6!

P.S. GUESS WHO GETS HOSED?

THEN THERE'S THE FAC WHO'S BIG ON TRIG — AT NIGHT, YET!

OKAY, COBRA LEAD, THE MARKERS ARE LYING NORTH-EAST TO SOUTHWEST, AND THEY ARE SOUTHEAST OF A ROAD THAT RUNS NORTHWEST TO SOUTHEAST. NOW, 1000 METERS FROM THE S.W. MARKER AND 1/3 THE DISTANCE BETWEEN THE MARKERS TO THE WEST OF THE NORTHEAST MARKER YOU...

HEY, LEAD! THEY REALLY SIEVED YOU ON THAT PASS!! NOW PUT YOUR NEXT BOMB 10 FEET TO THE LEFT OF THE LAST ONE!

THE LAST STRAW —
I WANT YOU TO GET THAT GUN SITE THAT JUST CHEWED UP THE F-4 FLIGHT AHEAD OF YOU ---

NAPALM ONLY

To tell the world in line-of-sight
That you're a horse's rear,
Just mash the mike before you think,
and everyone will hear.

THE GREAT 'HOT SHOT' PUT DOWN—

THE AIR HOG—

Psychologists, ponder!
And say, if you can:
Did the man make the hat,
Or the hat make the man?

AIRMEN'S HEADGEAR – WWII TYPE

FIRST SGTS AND CAMPAIGN HATS WERE MADE FOR EACH OTHER—

'TACTICAL OFFICERS' (GROUND POUNDERS) LOOKED LIKE THEY HAD A DISCUS IN THE BRIM

GREASE MONKEYS HAD THEIR 'SKIPPY' MODELS

ANYONE KNOW WHY THESE *6! DINKIES WERE CALLED 'OVERSEAS' CAPS?

GANG PLANK

THEN THERE WERE THOSE FLEECE-LINED BEAUTIES THAT ITCHED LIKE HELL.

TROPICS

BUT *NOTHING* COULD MATCH THE '50-MISSION CRUSH'!

HI YA, GIRLS!

We don't have room for Panel Five.
It shows the colonel, still alive,
Safely clad in a new flak vest —
Base commander at Bluie West...

THE BRIEFING —

GENTLEMEN, OUR TARGET FOR TODAY IS.....

RUHRFLACKEN!

IT'S GOING TO BE ROUGH, BUT WE'RE TOUGHER! WE'RE GOING TO GO RIGHT IN THERE THROUGH THAT FLAK and FIGHTERS AND WE'RE GOING TO LAY THOSE BOMBS RIGHT ON TARGET, AREN'T WE, MEN?!!

RIGHT!

UNFORTUNATELY, I WON'T BE GOING WITH YOU. HQS. HAS ORDERED ME TO REMAIN HERE, BUT, MY HEART WILL BE UP THERE WITH YOU ... ALL THE WAY!!

The customer is always right...
But if his finger's slightly nervous,
And clearly he's equipped to fight,
He may get extra service.

Ignorance was often bliss
and wisdom sometimes folly,
But angels all worked overtime —
And we won the war, by golly.

INSTRUMENT FLYING WAS NOT ONE OF OUR LONG SUITS IN WWII... AT LEAST FOR FIGHTER PILOTS.

ROGER, HOW MANY INSTRUMENT HOURS DID YOU SAY YOU HAD?

UH... WELL, LISSEE, COUNTING THIS TRIP- IF WE MAKE IT- *TWO*.

① ②

THEN THERE'S THE V.I.P. WHO SAID:

I SUPPOSE THIS MEANS WE'LL BE LATE IN GETTING TO SELFRIDGE!

This stereotype, slightly overripe,
May be viewed by some as a lot of tripe.
But though uniforms here are World War II,
Man/mission match still's generically true.

You've seen 'em in every club from Willy to Wiesbaden ---pick out the Ⓐ fighter jock Ⓑ bomber pilot Ⓒ transport driver Ⓓ special mission type Ⓔ bored bartender Ⓕ guy who got there early

How to terrify the free-loadin' ground pounders at just about liftoff speed –

Perils of instrument night approaches
Differ somewhat for players and coaches,
But for rapid aging, it's hard to beat
A spectator view from a damp right seat...

SUSPICIONS CONFIRMED—

IT'S A DARK and STORMY NIGHT; INSIDE THE SNUG GCA SHACK WE SEE—

UH...YER 50 FEET HIGH...NOW YER A HUNNERT FEET HIGH...COMING DOWN...WATCH IT...NOW YER GOING 50 FEET LOW...DECREASE YOUR RATE OF DESCENT...CORRECTING NICELY...OVER THE THRESHOLD...TAKE OVER VISUALLY FOR LANDING... I CALL

AVIATION GLOSSARY

ALTIMETER SETTING

'THE PLACE WHERE THE ALTIMETER SETS—USUALLY HIDDEN BEHIND THE CONTROL COLUMN DURING A TIGHT INSTRUMENT APPROACH'

THE CO-PILOT ON AN INSTRUMENT APPROACH

'CLEARED FOR APPROACH, CEILING 300, VIZ ½...'

'YOU'RE 200 FT. LOW...'

'APPROACHING MINIMUMS, STILL LOW'

'TAKE OVER and LAND VISUALLY'

See the foe of yesteryear,
The Kamikaze "volunteer."
See the T/O — also change.
The whole damned world's been rearranged...

OUR ADVERSARIES WERE AFFLICTED WITH THE SAME MENTAL AND PHYSICAL ABERRATIONS FACED BY G.I.s THE WORLD OVER--

BACK HOME IT WAS BUSINESS AS USUAL -

SOME THINGS *DO* CHANGE...

When one looks back in aviation it's not very far to the "buggy whip" stage. Consider, for example, that a mere 66 years separates man's first powered flight and landing on the moon!

POOR ROBERT'S 'ALMANACK'

1912 - A BUMPER CROP OF NEW AIRCRAFT COMPANIES SPRING UP. AMONG THE MORE NOTABLE WERE: *CRUMLEY MULTPLANE CO.', 'PEEKSKILL HYDROSEROPLANE CO.', 'REIFLIN HEADLESS AEROPLANE CO.'* (IT'S A FACT!)

THIS WAS THE 'BULLET' BUILT BY THE GALLAUDET ENGINEERING CO., SAID TO BE CAPABLE OF FLYING *100 mph!* (WITH A TAILWIND)

JUNE 2, 1924 - U.S. ARMY 'WORLD CRUISERS' BUILT BY DOUGLAS REACH JAPAN (THEY MADE IT CLEAR AROUND THE GLOBE, TOO - *IN 175 DAYS!*)

AT LAST! I WAS BEGINNIN' TO THINK THIS LAKE DIDN'T HAVE NO OTHER SIDE!

SAY, PAUL, WHAT'S THIS 'DEAD RECKONING'?

SIMPLE, YOU RECKON CORRECTLY OR YOU ARE.

AUG 17, 1927 - MARTIN JENSEN AND CAPT. PAUL SCHLUTER FLYING THE WRIGHT-POWERED 'ALOHA' ARE SECOND - AND *LAST* - IN THE DOLE OAKLAND-TO-HONOLULU RACE!

(OF 8 ENTRANTS, 4 CRASHED ON TAKEOFF AND 2 WERE LOST AT SEA... HOW ABOUT *THAT* FOR ODDS?!)

1929 FORD MOTOR CO., AIRPLANE DIV., EDSEL FORD PRESIDENT, BUILDS 5-AT MODEL TRI-MOTOR - LATEST IN A LONG SERIES THAT STARTED WITH THE LIBERTY-POWERED STOUT 2-AT

THAT GRILL DESIGN WILL GO DOWN IN HISTORY, EDSEL!

Gather round, you Big War jocks'
You guys who flew the Straight,
Or sweated out a Cobra, or left a '38.

Are all these stories true
about the vintage recips
You throttle-benders flew?

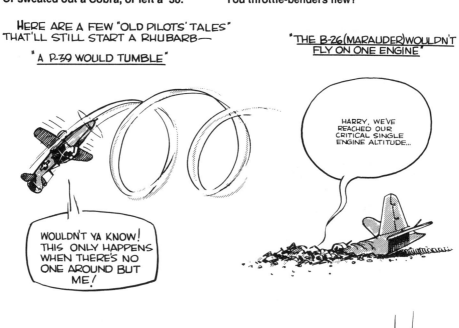

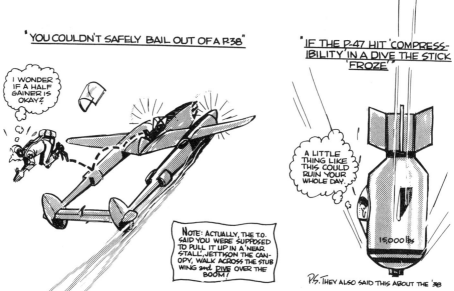

Turn with a zero it wouldn't.
Or climb with a sleek One-oh-nine.
But for busting tanks on the tundra
This baby really was fine...

THE P-39 (AIRACOBRA) 'THE BIRD NOBODY WANTED'

The Lightning's design was sure neat,
And its pilots were never effete.
But without jugs in the nose
To keep chill from toes
All Lightning jocks suffered cold feet...

THE 'LIGHTNING' WAS 'HOT' and COMPLICATED FOR ITS TIME. NEO-PHYTE JOCKS WERE USUALLY 'BE-HIND IT' THE FIRST 20 HRS OR SO---

YOU STILL THERE, LORD?

THE 4 30's and 20mm CANNON WERE MANUALLY CHARGED FROM THE COCKPIT. BALKY BREECHES CALLED FOR DRASTIC ACTION—

$40,000 FLIGHT TRAIN-ING TO BECOME A *@!m!! CANNON COCKER!

DON'T GIVE ME A P-38,
WITH PROPS THAT COUNTER-ROTATE,
THEY'LL LOOP, ROLL AND SPIN,
BUT THEY'LL SOON AUGER IN,
DON'T GIVE ME A P-38!
—OLD AAF BALLAD

CALLED 'WIDOW-MAKERS' BECAUSE OF A HIGH ACCIDENT RATE, ONE AAF CREWMAN PUT AN ERSATZ DIAL ON THE PANEL THAT SAID IT ALL—

SPIN BURN CRASH EXPLODE

PRE-SET BEFORE FLIGHT TO ELIMINATE GUESSWORK

BUT, REMEMBER, IT WAS THE ONLY AAF WWII FIGHTER THAT COULD COME HOME WITH A PROP FEATHERED!!

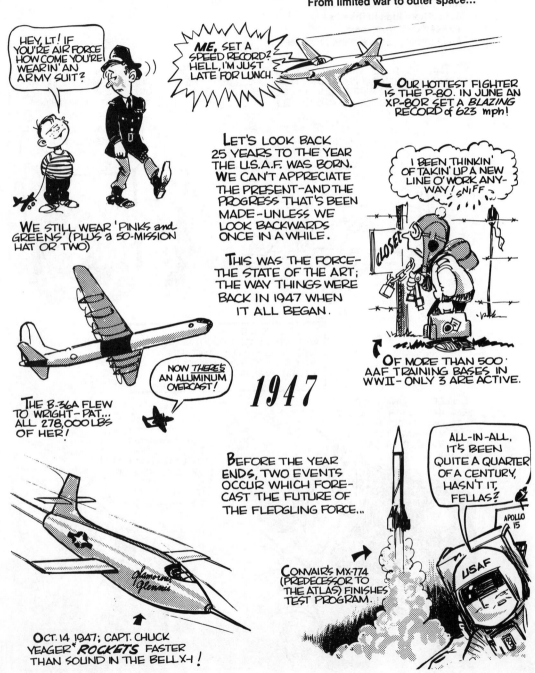

From P-51's to the F-15,
With muscles from missiles in between,
The Air Force has grown at a hectic pace —
From limited war to outer space...

HEY, LT! IF YOU'RE AIR FORCE HOW COME YOU'RE WEARIN' AN ARMY SUIT?

ME, SET A SPEED RECORD? HELL, I'M JUST LATE FOR LUNCH.

OUR HOTTEST FIGHTER IS THE P-80. IN JUNE AN XP-80R SET A BLAZING RECORD OF 623 mph!

WE STILL WEAR 'PINKS and GREENS' (PLUS A 50-MISSION HAT OR TWO)

LET'S LOOK BACK 25 YEARS TO THE YEAR THE U.S.A.F. WAS BORN. WE CAN'T APPRECIATE THE PRESENT—AND THE PROGRESS THAT'S BEEN MADE—UNLESS WE LOOK BACKWARDS ONCE IN A WHILE.

THIS WAS THE FORCE— THE STATE OF THE ART; THE WAY THINGS WERE BACK IN 1947 WHEN IT ALL BEGAN.

I BEEN THINKIN' OF TAKIN' UP A NEW LINE O' WORK ANY- WAY! SNIFF

CLOSED

OF MORE THAN 500 AAF TRAINING BASES IN WWII— ONLY 3 ARE ACTIVE.

NOW THERE'S AN ALUMINUM OVERCAST!

THE B-36A FLEW TO WRIGHT-PAT... ALL 278,000 LBS OF HER!

1947

BEFORE THE YEAR ENDS, TWO EVENTS OCCUR WHICH FORE- CAST THE FUTURE OF THE FLEDGLING FORCE...

ALL-IN-ALL, IT'S BEEN QUITE A QUARTER OF A CENTURY, HASN'T IT, FELLAS?

APOLLO 15

USAF

CONVAIR'S MX-774 (PREDECESSOR TO THE ATLAS) FINISHES TEST PROGRAM.

Glamorous Glennis

OCT. 14 1947; CAPT. CHUCK YEAGER* ROCKETS FASTER THAN SOUND IN THE BELL X-1!

To sleep, perchance to dream. Aye, there's the rub —
I cannot beat the major with a club!
With all his wrinkles, bags and rank,
I cannot say, "You and this whole trip stank!"

New second Johns thought her a sentence of doom —
Not many runways then had enough room.
But once in the air, with a pair of fans turning,
Brother, this baby just kept on churning...

THE MARTIN B-26 'MARAUDER'
'THE FLYING PROSTITUTE'
(IT HAD NO VISIBLE MEANS OF SUPPORT)

PILOT'S IMPRESSION OF EARLY '26 –

ENGINES, TWO BIG and TOO HEAVY

OUR FATHER WHO ART IN

IRONING BOARDS FOR WINGS

TONS and TONS OF AMMUNITION

RUNWAY, TOO SHORT

SHUDDER

STAGGER

'A PLANE A DAY IN TAMPA BAY' WAS THE CRY FROM A NEARBY B-26 'RUSH' PILOT TRAINING BASE –

NOW I KNOW WHY THEY CALL IT THE FLYIN' TORPEDO!!

I WANTED WINGS

"...I DON'T WANT TO TOUR OVER BERLIN OR THE RUHR
ACK ACK ALWAYS MAKES ME LOSE MY LUNCH
FOR THERE'S NO HEY HEY WHEN THEY HOLLER 'BOMBS AWAY'!
I'D RATHER BE HOME WITH THE BUNCH..."

OLD AAF SONG

FLYING AT MURDEROUSLY MEDIUM ALTITUDES, 26'S ATTRACTED FLAK LIKE A MAGNET –

ULP! A GUY COULD GET OUT and WALK ON THAT FLAK!

397TH BOMB GP. MARKINGS

Flak Bait

HELL, YES, WE GOT PROBLEMS! SEND US MORE OF THE DAMNED AIRPLANES!

BOMB TONNAGE

ACCIDENTS   MAINT

CO. 22ND BOMB GP.

NOTE: DESPITE EARLY PROBLEMS THE 'MYSTICAL MARAUDER' TURNED IN AN UNPARALLED COMBAT RECORD!

Pop, Pop, Sputter, Bang
Is the Maytag going to prang?
Sputter, Sputter, Bang, Bump!
I thought the pilot said to jump!

BRIEFING FOR OUR FIRST NIGHT DUAL RIDE – PRIMARY FLYING SCHOOL, DOS PALOS, CALIF. (1942)

NOW REMEMBER! IF THAT ENGINE QUITS, *and* I INDICATE 'BAIL OUT', YOU *LEAVE!* GOT THAT, DUMBJOHN?

Y-YES, SIR.

AND SO IT CAME TO PASS THAT THEY LEAPED OFF IN THEIR 'MAYTAG MESSERSCHMITTS' (PT-22's)

HEADS UP NOW, DUMBJOHN!

OUR INSTRUCTOR IS OVERCOME WITH THE BEAUTY OF THE NIGHT... DUMBJOHN CAN'T HEAR SO THE BOSS THROTTLES BACK, AND...

I SAID, ISN'T DOS PALOS PRETTY AT NIGHT?!

POP

SPUT

LOOSE GOSPORT *and* CONNECTION BETWEEN THE EARS

BANG

YEP, YOU GUESSED IT—

DOS PALOS BIJOU

GONE WITH THE WIND

Previously, we touched on how to bail out of a P-38. This brought forth a pilot's manual which contained — honest Injun — the quotes below.

ON BAILING OUT—

" ONCE YOU HAVE STARTED FALLING YOUR FIRST INCLINATION MAY BE TO SEE HOW FAST YOU CAN GET THAT CHUTE OPEN. IF THIS IS YOUR INCLINATION— *CONTROL IT!* "

" THE IMPORTANT THING TO RE-MEMBER IS: DO NOT RISK DAMAGING YOUR CHUTE BY OPENING IT AT HIGH SPEEDS "

WHAT ABOUT *ME* DUM – DUM ?

WHOMP!

EDITOR'S NOTE: THIS IS GUARAN-TEED TO MAKE A SOPRANO OUT OF YOU!

" SOME PILOTS STILL BELIEVE THAT OLD FABLE ABOUT COUNTING THREE WHEN PULLING. FOR OUR MONEY THAT IS JUST ANOTHER RUMOR "

T- T- T- TWO...

"WHENEVER POSSIBLE WAIT UNTIL YOU GET THAT 'OLD FLOATING FEELING' "

We've sometimes wondered if the armament chief
Lives on a diet of uncooked beef.
Here we learn that his temper — seldom stable —
Has been fragged by the ops guys, not by the table!

THE ARMAMENT CHIEF

Here, barracks wisdom we distill —
If things can go amiss, they will...
A foe misjudged will get the kill —

Rank had its dues, and has 'em still...
And you, my son, need never fear
If you neglect to volunteer!

Forgive the IPs lots of tricks
From which these monsters get their kicks,
But here's a ploy that's just too shoddy,
So, Sarge, let's jettison the body...

SCENE: THE COCKPIT OF A B-26 ON A TRANSITION RIDE. SHORTLY AFTER TAKEOFF THE IP MAKES HIS MOVE—

LET'S SEE WHAT HOTSHOT CHARLIE CAN DO ON ONE ENGINE.

HELP ME HOLD HER, SIR!!

I CAN'T. I'M DEAD. DO EXACTLY WHAT YOU WOULD DO IN COMBAT!

SARGE, GET THAT DEAD S.O.B. OUTTA HERE and HELP ME HOLD THIS BEAST!!

Poor Robert's "Almanack"
A look at fighters — men and machines —1917 to date.

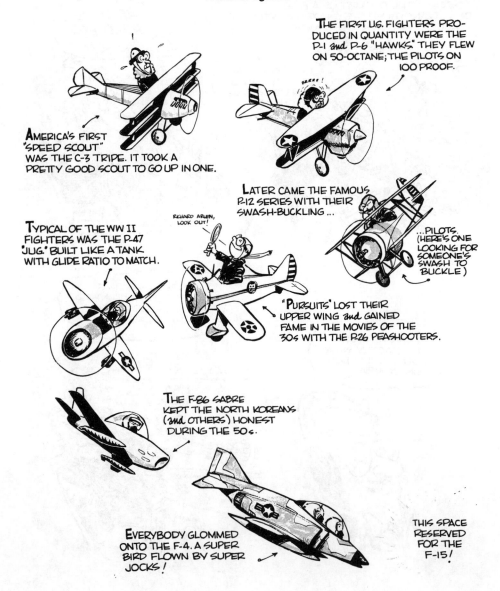

THE FIRST U.S. FIGHTERS PRODUCED IN QUANTITY WERE THE P-1 and P-6 "HAWKS." THEY FLEW ON 50-OCTANE; THE PILOTS ON 100 PROOF.

BRRRR!

AMERICA'S FIRST "SPEED SCOUT" WAS THE C-3 TRIPE. IT TOOK A PRETTY GOOD SCOUT TO GO UP IN ONE.

LATER CAME THE FAMOUS P-12 SERIES WITH THEIR SWASH-BUCKLING ...

...PILOTS. (HERE'S ONE LOOKING FOR SOMEONE'S SWASH TO BUCKLE)

TYPICAL OF THE WW II FIGHTERS WAS THE P-47 "JUG." BUILT LIKE A TANK WITH GLIDE RATIO TO MATCH.

RICHARD ARLEN, LOOK OUT!

"PURSUITS" LOST THEIR UPPER WING and GAINED FAME IN THE MOVIES OF THE 30s WITH THE P-26 PEASHOOTERS.

THE F-86 SABRE KEPT THE NORTH KOREANS (and OTHERS) HONEST DURING THE 50s.

EVERYBODY GLOMMED ONTO THE F-4. A SUPER BIRD FLOWN BY SUPER JOCKS!

THIS SPACE RESERVED FOR THE F-15!

Although your record's quite impressive,
Your arrogance now seems excessive.
When tallying this morning's score
One's as good as sixty-four!

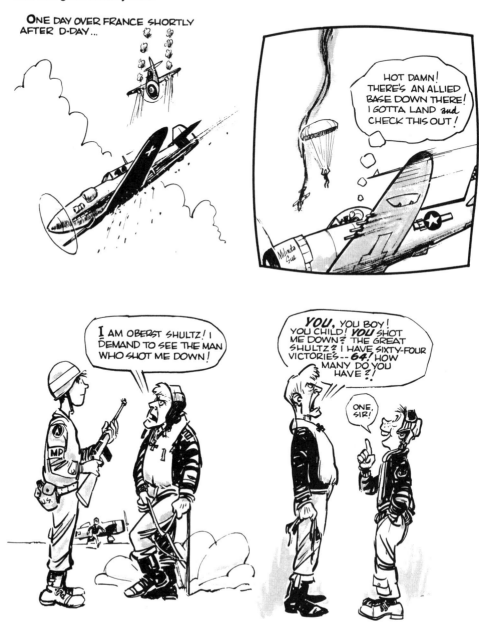

When the work's all done at evening,
When they've beat the Zeke's attacks,
And the morrow is a stand-down,
Then the fighter jocks relax.

And if, around the squadron bar.
Some overly unbend,
They'll leave that last long runway —
Fighter pilots to the end.

A bold, free spirit charging fierce
Across the fallow land
And don't you like these nice white flowers
I'm holding in my hand?

These are excerpts of "orders" given to Confederate Air Force crews for a flight from Rebel Field, Harlingen, Texas to Wright-Pat. Our thanks to "Col. Throckmorton T. Beauregard, CAF" for this aviation classic.

"Any aircraft with operational compass may serve as flight leader. (Charts published prior to 1936 are not considered reliable and should not be used.) . . . Compass heading 10° to 60° mag. approx. Your route will take you over six states; Okla. is the green one; Missouri is brown; Ill. is yellow; Ind. is red, and Ohio is the tan one on your Texaco map. Care must be used at intersection of US 66 and US 40 east of St. Louis--stay on US 40."

Preflight--
"Next, check stick and throttle positions. If the stick is in your left hand and the throttle is in your right hand, you are in the cockpit backwards. Don't panic! Smile at the crew chief, wave to bystanders and slowly rotate your body 180°."

"When signal is given to taxi, advance the throttle smoothly, hit the 'highblower' switch and jump smoothly over the chocks. Retard the throttle to military power and try to avoid further use of highblower while taxiing as this irritates ground personnel."

"After leaving the ground, pull the nose up smartly, close your eyes and count 10. If contact with the ground has not occurred by that time, continue the mission as briefed. (Note: You may open your eyes for the remainder of the flight if you wish--however, this is optional.)"

Rest and Recreation was its official name
Now the title's changed tho' the purpose is the same.
To the men it's R and R — those letters stand for fun.
But to the friendly natives it means "Romp and Run".

REMEMBER HOW IT WAS *GOING* ON R and R ?...

AND COMING BACK ?

EINSTEIN WAS RIGHT—
TIME *and* DISTANCE
CAN CHANGE MATTER.

LORRY STOP

WHAT SHE *REALLY* LOOKED LIKE

IN THE PACIFIC THEATER IT WAS HARD TO TELL WHEN A GUY HAD BEEN ON R and R—

BEFORE

AFTER

THE "ASIATIC" STARE (LOOK-ING 20 YDS IN A 20 FT. ROOM.

THE "WHAT-THE-HELL-AM-I-DOING-BACK-HERE-I-COULD-GET-KILLED" LOOK.

Glory! No more regulations...
Rip them down in all the stations!
Ground the guy that tries to make one!
AND LET US ALL FLY LIKE HELL!
                        -Old AAF Song

AT A FORWARD FIRE BASE DURING THE MOST RECENT UNPLEASANTNESS—

BUSHWHACK, THIS IS AIRWING RED ONE—HOW DOES IT LOOK DOWN THERE?

OKAY. COME ON IN. NO VC.

IF THAT'S SO, HOW COME YOU'RE WHISPERING THEN?

THEN THERE WAS THE NEWLY-MINTED 2ND LT.—NAVIGATOR TYPE—WHO SHOWED UP AT BASE OPERATIONS FULLY OUTFITTED FOR A SCHEDULED FLIGHT—

BUT I THOUGHT WE WERE GOING TO IRAN!!

WE ARE. IRAN* IS AT BURBANK.

*INSPECT and REPAIR As NECESSARY

AND IN CADETS, YOU COULD ALWAYS SCARE HELL OUT OF YOURSELF and THE INSTRUCTOR BY SWITCHING TO AN EMPTY TANK IN THE PATTERN PULLING THE GUMP CHECK—

Gas
Undercarriage
Mixture
Prop

POP! BANG!

Both of these stories are true, my friend,
And Merced Field was the place.
We yearn to be a dumbjohn again —
Our motto? "Each man an Ace!"

THEN THERE WAS "DER INSTRUKTOR" (A CADET) WHO ENTERTAINED CLASS 43E – VIA RADIO:

Early in WW II there was a lot of hysteria and misinformation about Japanese aircraft and pilots. Since the rather fragile Zero could outclimb the P-40 and Japanese pilots rarely attacked unless the advantage was clearly theirs (not a bad idea), PR types had a field day.

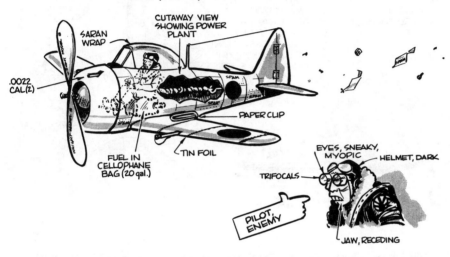

ZERO (THEIRS)

SARAN WRAP

CUTAWAY VIEW SHOWING POWER PLANT

.0022 CAL (2)

SPAM

PAPER CLIP

TIN FOIL

FUEL IN CELLOPHANE BAG (20 gal.)

EYES, SNEAKY, MYOPIC

HELMET, DARK

TRIFOCALS

PILOT, ENEMY

JAW, RECEDING

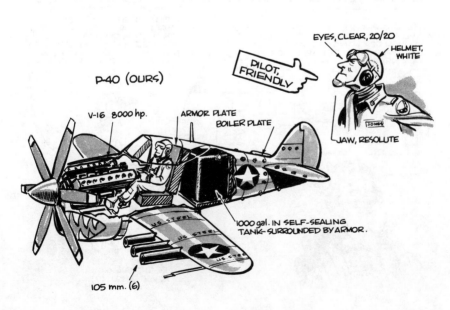

EYES, CLEAR, 20/20

HELMET, WHITE

DILOT, FRIENDLY

P-40 (OURS)

V-16 8000 hp.

ARMOR PLATE

BOILER PLATE

JAW, RESOLUTE

JONES

1000 gal. IN SELF-SEALING TANK SURROUNDED BY ARMOR.

US STEEL

105 mm. (6)

We've had fuel shortages before. For awhile in WW II there wasn't enough 100/130 to fill a Zippo. Higher HQ — in its infinite wisdom — substituted 91 octane for 100/130 in the States. Dubbed "Operation Prang" by pilots, it scattered men and machines from Bangor to Baja.

FUEL SHORTAGES

By the ring around his eyeball
You can tell a bombardier.
You can tell a bomber pilot
By the spread around his rear.

You can tell a navigator
By his sextants, maps and such.
You can tell a fighter jocky —
BUT YOU CAN'T TELL HIM MUCH!

Missing an easy enemy kill
May be cause for colossal chagrin.
But nothing at all like a critical call
When a fighter jock's all buckled in.

Most airmen recognize the familiar production models of AAF WW II aircraft. Here are a few little-known experimental beauties than barely got off the drawing board.

POOR ROBERT'S "ALMANACK" (Vol. 5)

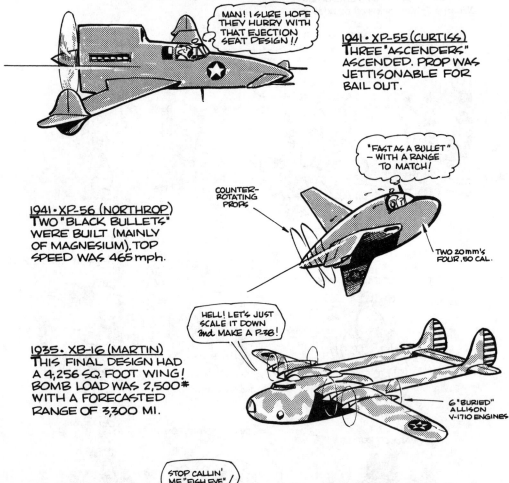

1941 • XP-55 (CURTISS)
THREE "ASCENDERS" ASCENDED. PROP WAS JETTISONABLE FOR BAIL OUT.

1941 • XP-56 (NORTHROP)
TWO "BLACK BULLETS" WERE BUILT (MAINLY OF MAGNESIUM). TOP SPEED WAS 465 mph.

1935 • XB-16 (MARTIN)
THIS FINAL DESIGN HAD A 4,256 SQ. FOOT WING! BOMB LOAD WAS 2,500# WITH A FORECASTED RANGE OF 3,300 MI.

1943 • XB-42 (DOUGLAS)
THE "MIXMASTER" FIRST FLEW IN 1944. TWO WERE BUILT—BOTH EVENTUALLY PRANGED. FAST and ABLE TO CARRY A BIG LOAD. END OF WAR CANCELLED MASS PRODUCTION PLANS.

We quote some gems from that venerable Confederate Air Force flight order, (issued from "The Octagon") to rebel flight crews for a flight to Wright-Pat. in May 1967.

THE PREFLIGHT

(1) Approach the aircraft in a reckless, devil-may-care manner, as this makes a big impression on bystanders. . . . Ask the nearest small boy what type aircraft this is— just to make sure.

(2) Check all fuel tanks to see if the air has been removed therefrom. Be sure to kick all tires vigorously. When you come to a complicated part of the airplane, stare at it seriously for several seconds. . . . This creates a favorable impression on your crew chief. . . .

(3) When you have finished the preflight, ask another bystander what aircraft this is. Then proceed rapidly to your assigned aircraft and repeat steps 1 and 2.

(4) To enter the aircraft, approach it from the left side and leap lightly onto the access ladder without looking. Then pick yourself up off the ground in a casual manner, locate the ladder, and climb the steps. . . .

P.S. To control acrophobia, don't look down when going up the ladder!

At the risk of starting a rhubarb with navigators, this story *had* to be told. Equal space is granted on the following pages to navigators who demanded (very vocally, I might add) rebuttal time.

The story below — which might have been entitled "How I Learned to Stop Using the Gunsight for a Crutch and Start Living" — is true. I hope the principal character is still with us!

All air services used the venerable "T-Bird." The first TP-80C (redesignated T-33A) came off the line in 1947. It has been with us ever since and many a pilot cut his jet teeth on this fine machine.

REMEMBER...

GEEZ! WHAT GRACE, WHAT FORM!

...A TAKEOFF ATTEMPT WITH THE NOSEWHEEL COCKED?

...SNOW IN THE COCKPIT– *IN JULY?*
(IT WAS THE AIR CONDITIONER – PARTICULARLY ON HOT, HUMID DAYS)

A TRAIN? BEHIND ME?...AT *THIS* ALTITUDE?

WHEEEEE! RUMBLE! SQUEEE TOOT!

...DUCT RUMBLE and OTHER "SPOOK" NOISES?

"VERTICAL FLIGHT AXIS INDICATOR"?
(YAW STRING WITH A KNOT IN IT!)

...YOUR VIEW FROM THE REAR SEAT ON FINAL WITH A STUDENT PILOT UP FRONT?

MUST BE A CHECKOUT.

WORST CASE O' WING WALKIN' I'VE EVER SEEN!

...YOUR FIRST EXPOSURE TO AILERON BOOST?

Once upon a time there was a regulation which permitted an AAF pilot to take his wife, and certain other relatives, for a ride in a military aircraft (one flight per year). This is a true story of one such flight.

A-24 (NAVY VERSION: SPD) LOOKED and FLEW LIKE A SOUPED-UP T-6.

Navigators, zapped previously, responded with vigor. The hail of flak from the Sextant and Bubble Corps about the pint-sized fighter jock is depicted below.

Rivalry between bomber and fighter pilots is legend. A particularly spirited rivalry existed between the 78th Ftr. Gp., based at Duxford, Station 357, and the 91st Bomb Gp. (H), based at Bassingbourn, Station 121, in Jolly Old...

IT ALL STARTED WHEN "REDLINE", CANINE MASCOT OF THE 91st, WAS SPIRITED AWAY DURING A JOINT PARTY.

SHHH! THROW 'IM ANOTHER BONE!

ROWRF!

THE WAR ENDED (WITH "REDLINE" STILL MIA) and THE AIR FORCE GOT BACK TO SPIT and POLISH PARADES –

OH, OH, HERE COMES A 91st '17 WITH THE BOMB DOORS OPEN.

I DON'T LIKE THE LOOKS OF THIS.

78 FTR GRP

HORSE MANURE! A HALF TON OF IT!!

THOSE LOUSY ⊙ ✳ !⚊✦ !!⑤✳! ...JUST WAIT'LL WE GET THEM!

THE 91st WAITED WITH BATED BREATH TO SEE WHAT FORM RETALIATION WOULD TAKE. THE NEXT DAY A LONE '51 DROPPED A WREATH AT BASSINGBOURN.

IN MEMORY OF YOUR COMMANDING OFFICER WHO YESTERDAY, OVER DUXFORD, FELL FROM ONE OF YOUR AIRCRAFT.

IN MEMORIAM

Regulations "Concerning the Operation of Aircraft" as set forth by the United States Air Service in the year 1920.

Scenes like this raise the "pucker factor" to its zenith and make a fellow a trifle edgy. The co-pilot just caught his sleeve in the throttle quadrant as a cannon shell burst in the cockpit and has been screaming, "I'm paralyzed!"

Soviet and U.S. airmen met each other on few occasions during "The Big One". One place was Alaska where the U.S.S.R. took delivery of lend-lease aircraft. Another was in Russia itself on the U.S. shuttle raids over Eastern Europe.

THIS ALLEGEDLY TRUE STORY INVOLVED A NEWLY-MINTED 2ND LT. CHECKING OUT A SOVIET PILOT IN THE B-25:

OKAY, LT. IVAN, CLIMB STRAIGHT OUT...

HOKAY!

THEN IVAN ROLLS IT!

ULP!

WASSAMATTER? YOU 'FRAID TO DIE?

KEEP OUT GOVT. PROP FAIRBANKS AAB

ON A SHUTTLE RAID TO POLTAVA, U.S.S.R., ONE OF THE FIRST P-38s IN WAS MISTAKEN FOR A GERMAN FW 189.

HE SAYS, COMRADE AMERIKANSKI, THEY SHOOT—THEN IDENTIFY!

MORE RECENTLY, ATTEMPTS BY U.S. FIGHTER PILOTS TO HAND SIGNAL INTERCEPTED SOVIET "BEAR" BOMBERS HAVE FAILED. ONE TECHNIQUE, HOWEVER, ALWAYS WORKS—

GIB (GUY IN THE BACK SEAT) HOLDING UP CENTERSPREAD OF PLAYBOY

This classic airman's story had its origin in the Panama Canal Zone during WW II where a bunch of bored P-39 and P-40 jocks stood "submarine alert"…

Fighter jocks are a vocal lot — especially when it comes to the pros and cons of their particular steed of the moment. The "Jug", alias P-47, had many devotees, but there were a few malcontents. One thing everyone agreed on: it was big and heavy.

MAKING AN INSTRUMENT APPROACH CONSISTED OF TOSSING A BRICK OUT OVER THE RADIO CONE OF SILENCE and THEN FLYING FORMATION WITH IT —

OVERHEARD AT THE O'CLUB BAR—

OKAY, HOTSHOT! SO YOUR '51 CAN ACCELERATE FASTER THAN MY JUG, BUT I'LL BETCHA I CAN OUTFALL YA!

IT WAS ALLEGED THAT THE HEAVILY ARMORED JUG'S HIGH KILL RATIO WAS ACCOMPLISHED BY GETTING IN FRONT OF THE ENEMY and...

HEH, HEH, HE'LL RUN OUT OF AMMO and FUEL—THEN I GOT 'IM!

(and THERE WAS ALWAYS THE POSSIBILITY THE HUNTER MIGHT RUN INTO ONE OF HIS OWN RICOCHETS!, ED.)

LONG-RANGE ESCORT VERSIONS OF THE '47 GOT PRETTY FANCY.

LOOK HOW CALM THEM FIGHTER PILOTS ARE!

ZAWP!

FOLD-DOWN PADDED RUDDER PEDALS
AUTO PILOT
VIBRATING SEAT

It's about time we recognized those unsung heroes of EC (stands for Electronic Counter measures). The old "humpback" AKA EC-121 Super Connie, or "swineicus subsonicus" as referred to by her crews, has been doing a super job for several decades. But there is one thing about the old girl, she's slow. As a matter of fact, pilots who wrote songs about her in the southeast Asian theatre of war often referred to her as the "Lockheed flying speedbrake."

65 GALLONS OF CRUDDY OIL PER ENGINE EMITTED

Your view on how the air war should have been fought in Europe depended on your rank, number of missions under your belt, and your position in the formation. Take, f'instance...

A NEW B/G COMMANDER OF A B-17 WING APPROACHING A REAL NASTY TARGET FOR THE FIRST TIME...

AWRIGHT, YOU DIRTY KRAUTS, COME UP and FIGHT!!

and FAR BEHIND IN THE BOMBER STREAM WE HEAR FROM A 1ST JOHN ON HIS 24TH MISSION...

DON'T LISSEN TO HIM FELLAS! THIS IS ONLY A PRACTICE MISSION FOR FLIGHT PAY! FOR C___'S SAKE STAY DOWN!

THEN THERE WAS THE HARRIED LIB CREW TAKING A LOT OF FLAK, CO-PILOT OUT and A BLOWN #4...

QUICK, ENGINEER, FEATHER FOUR!!

(GETTING 4 FINGERS READY FOR THE BUTTONS)

...YEP, YOU GUESSED IT!

OH FER ⊙✳☜✴○!

SPUT!

POP!

LIBERATOR CLUB P.O. BOX 841 SAN DIEGO, CA. 92112

B-24 GLIDING ANVIL

In response to the overwhelming demand (some guy said "Hey, whatever happened to...?") we herewith give you another series of those zany gems found in the Confederate Air Force official glossary of aviation terms.

ENGINE FAILURE

A CONDITION WHICH OCCURS WHEN ALL FUEL TANKS BECOME FILLED WITH AIR.

COMPENSATING THE COMPASS

A RITUAL PERFORMED BY PILOTS AFTER EMERGING FROM A CLOUD BANK.

LANDING FLAP

A 6,000-FT LANDING ROLL ON A 5,000-FT RUNWAY.

"CLEAR!"

WARNING SHOUTED TWO SECONDS AFTER YOU HIT THE STARTER BUTTON.

Communication was always a bit chancy in early flying machines. Lack of same was not *always* due to equipment malfunction, however. Our story takes place at an advanced flight training base, class 44F.

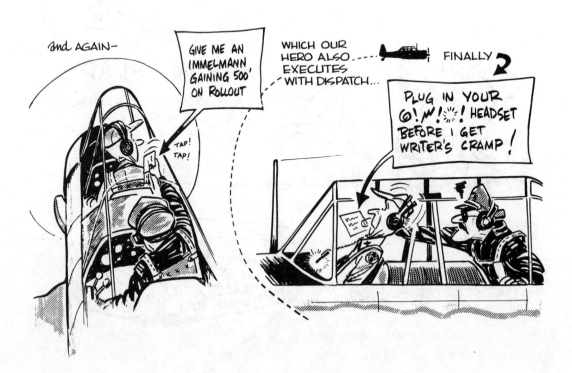

The T-37 "Tweety Bird" — or as it is often referred to, "The Converter" (it converts fuel into noise) — started life as a USAF trainer. During 'nam it was pressed into service as the A-37 *Dragonfly* where it performed attack missions in a very commendable fashion.

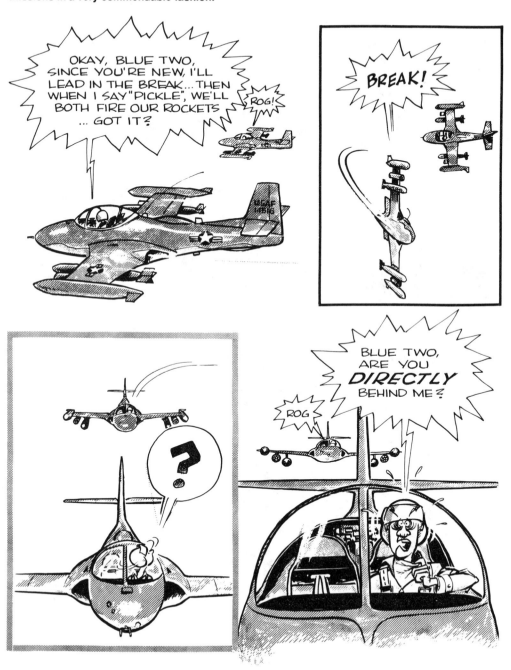

"Silence is golden" according to an early Swiss inscription. Silence is also *mandatory* in Air Force formations from home base to the target (the enemy had ears, too). This is an old tale and it *could* have happened — and near Swiss territory, for that matter.

Since an increasing number of German NATO and civilian pilots are training in this country, U.S. controllers and aviators will find the following illustrated glossary helpful.

GEFRACTURED GERMAN GLOSSARY FÜR GEFLIEGERS
PART I

Der fliegenwagen (das ist eine kleine fliegenwagen)

Der tailschwingen pushen-pullen werker.

Der airfloggenfan

Der pushenpullen schtick

Der tailschwingen werks

Der grosser fliegenwagen mit drei airfloggenfannen

UND ALSO CHECKEN DER ÖL, MEIN KAPITAN?

Iron Annie

N. CAIDIN PROP.

Airshow '75 Confederate AF Harlingen, Tex.

Der dummkopfs schtuck mit der tailschwingen pushenpullen werker

to be continued ~

Part I covered "fliegenwagens" of WW I and pre-WW II. Now, students, we will describe the intricacies of operating WW II aircraft. Please take notes — we may ask questions later.

GEFRACTURED GERMAN GLOSSARY FÜR GEFLIEGERS
PART II

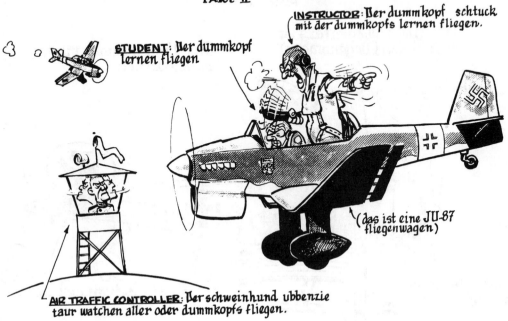

STUDENT: Der dummkopf lernen fliegen

INSTRUCTOR: Der dummkopf schtuck mit der dummkopfs lernen fliegen.

(das ist eine JU-87 fliegenwagen)

AIR TRAFFIC CONTROLLER: Der schweinhund ubbenzie taur watchen aller oder dummkopfs fliegen.

IFR: Lissenwaitenhopen fliegen.

JET AIRCRAFT: Der fliegenwagen mit sckullschplitten schraemen spitten firenbakof en-smoken.

das ist alles...

Stories like this tend to gain credibility when told and retold. As a matter of fact, one story I originated many years ago came back to me in the form of a real life experience to a pilot in southeast Asia. This T-6 blooper actually happened. I imagine both of the pilots involved made a silken descent.

Great air battles were often fought in officer club bars among crewmen. Most such battles were won — and a few were lost.

THEN THERE WAS THE QUEASY NON-RATED MAJOR RIDING IN THE BACK OF A B-25 WHO WAS TOLD BY A CREWMAN:

Now it can be revealed — the real nomenclature of World War II fighter! We provide you aircraft historians this phantom cut-away drawing showing the intricacies of a typical warbird. These are the official terms of the Confederate Air Force which, they report, have been stolen from only the most authentic publications.

CUTAWAY – WW II FIGHTER (OURS)

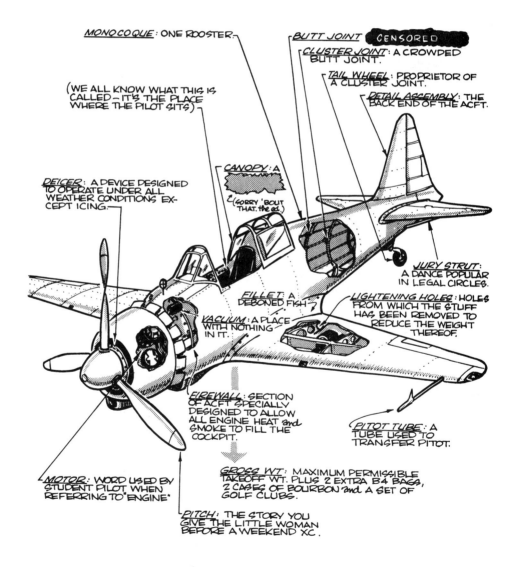

MONOCOQUE: ONE ROOSTER.

BUTT JOINT CENSORED

CLUSTER JOINT: A CROWDED BUTT JOINT.

TAIL WHEEL: PROPRIETOR OF A CLUSTER JOINT.

(WE ALL KNOW WHAT THIS IS CALLED – IT'S THE PLACE WHERE THE PILOT SITS)

DETAIL ASSEMBLY: THE BACK END OF THE ACFT.

DEICER: A DEVICE DESIGNED TO OPERATE UNDER ALL WEATHER CONDITIONS EXCEPT ICING.

CANOPY: A (SORRY 'BOUT THAT. the ed.)

JURY STRUT: A DANCE POPULAR IN LEGAL CIRCLES.

FILLET: A DEBONED FISH

LIGHTENING HOLES: HOLES FROM WHICH THE STUFF HAS BEEN REMOVED TO REDUCE THE WEIGHT THEREOF.

VACUUM: A PLACE WITH NOTHING IN IT.

FIREWALL: SECTION OF ACFT SPECIALLY DESIGNED TO ALLOW ALL ENGINE HEAT and SMOKE TO FILL THE COCKPIT.

PITOT TUBE: A TUBE USED TO TRANSFER PITOT.

MOTOR: WORD USED BY STUDENT PILOT WHEN REFERRING TO "ENGINE".

GROSS WT: MAXIMUM PERMISSIBLE TAKEOFF WT. PLUS 2 EXTRA B4 BAGS, 2 CASES OF BOURBON and A SET OF GOLF CLUBS.

PITCH: THE STORY YOU GIVE THE LITTLE WOMAN BEFORE A WEEKEND XC.

"Communicate — v.t. 1 To give to another — impart; transmit." Webster doesn't say anything about *receiving* and that, dear readers, is the subject of this cartoon. Thomas Fuller, the famous author said it all in, "Birds are entangled by their feet and men by their tongues."

1943-A P-70 * IS OVER GUADALCANAL CHASING THE ELUSIVE "WASHING MACHINE CHARLIE" AT ANGELS 20 - OXYGEN IS RUNNING LOW...

HEY, BUDDY, WE AIN'T HAD A LIL' OL' VECTOR FROM GROUN' CONTROL "KIWI" FER A LONG TIME *

RADAR OPERATOR

* NIGHT-FIGHTER VERSION OF DOUGLAS A-20 HAVOC.

ROGER, OL' TROOP. MUSH BE TH' RADIO ANTENNA'S SHOT AGIN... WE BETTER PANCAKE *

H'LO KIWI. THIS ISH RED ONE. OUR ANTENNA ISH BROKEN and WE CAN'T TRANSHMIT. OVER

* LAND

ROGER, RED ONE. UNDERSTAND YOU ARE UNABLE TO TRANSMIT. RETURN TO BASE and PANCAKE.

ROGER, KIWI.

* SHOUNDS REASHONABLE T'ME...

OR HOW ABOUT THIS NEWER GEM ? :

AIR FORCE ONE NINER FIVER HOLDING AT TWO ZERO THOUSAND, I CAN EXPEDITE YOUR APPROACH IF YOU CAN DESCEND TO TWO THOUSAND IN TWO MINUTES.

NO SWEAT, APPROACH, CAN DO — BUT I WON'T HAVE NO AIRPLANE WITH ME WHEN I GET THERE!

In this episode we deal with what fighter jocks referred to as "Big Friends." And they *were* big in many ways — especially in the fortitude (or "guts") department. Here's to the crews of all those forts, libs and '29's!

HOW CUM? THE POWERS THAT BE – IN THEIR INFINITE WISDOM –ALWAYS SELECTED THE RIGHT PHYSIQUE FOR THE JOB AT HAND? TAKE THIS B-17 CREW, F'INSTANCE:

BOMBARDIER	NAVIGATOR	PILOT	COPILOT	ENGINEER	BALLTURRET	RADIO	WAIST GUNNERS	TAIL GUNNER
TWEEDLE DEE HERE HAD TO SHOEHORN INTO THIS OFFICE	*and* DUM	THE HEADMAN IS CARRYING 2 CUSHIONS TO SEE OUT		(ALSO UPPER TURRET GUNNER)	HE "SQUOZE" INTO THIS THING	"—.•" OL'BOY	(WHOSE BEHINDS ALWAYS MET AMIDSHIPS IN BATTLE)	"CHARLIE" WENT IN HERE

IT'S NOSTALGIA TIME, *REMEMBER...?*

...A FROSTY ENGLISH MORN AT 3AM, THE NISSEN HUT DOOR SQUEAKS OPEN *and* THE "WAKE-UP SGT." STARTS THE ROLL-OUT FOR THE DAY'S MISSION?

...TRYING TO GET A CUPPA COFFEE DOWN AFTER YOUR FIRST 10-HR MISSION?

...SURVIVING 25 *and* GETTING ONE OF THESE?

NEXT?

(BEEN LIKE A TREE FULL OF OWLS FOR 2 HRS)

JONES, F. R

HEY KID! TRY A SHOT OF "MEDICINAL SPIRITS" FIRST.

Once upon a time there were NCO pilots -- "flying sergeants." They flew anything that had wings and was painted olive drab. They are a proud lot and have formed a strong post-war association.

This episode might be entitled "Chicken in the Sky." We deal with the innermost thoughts of man...a pretty terrifying subject, at best. Wordsworth pegged it with,"Voyaging through strange seas of thought, alone."

Fighter pilots, being fighter pilots, are wont to engage in aerobatics at the drop of a bomb to impress their brethren in the bigger iron birds. The "big friends" have a few impressive maneuvers of their own.

This story was told to me at a reunion of World War II night fighters in Colorado Springs several years ago. Night flying — and fighting — takes a special breed of cat!

TRUE STORY: TOWER HAD TO REPEAT WARNING INSTRUCTIONS RE 200' TREES 800' OFF END OF ONE RUNWAY; THE INEVITABLE HAPPENED —

BLAZER 28, WISH TO ADVISE THERE ARE **800 FT.** TREES 200 FT. OFF APPROACH END OF RUNWAY...CLEARED TO LAND.

ROGER, TOWER, ON THE 800 FT. TREES! HOW *THICK* ARE THEY?

THEN THERE WAS THE MOTHER WHO VISITED HER SON'S WW II OUTFIT *and* WASN'T OVERLY IMPRESSED BY THE NOSE ART.

NITE TAKEOFF

"WELL, IT'S ALL VERY NICE, SONNY, BUT I DIDN'T NOTICE ANY PICTURES OF THE PILOT'S *MOTHERS* UP THERE!"

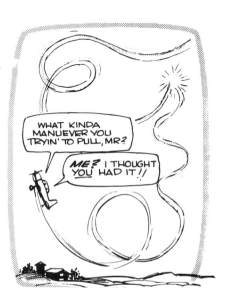

WHAT KINDA MANUEVER YOU TRYIN' TO PULL, MR?

ME? I THOUGHT *YOU* HAD IT!!

More regulations concerning the Operation of Aircraft (1920). "If you see another machine, get out of its way" is very basic to all flying — it is responsible for a huge radar net and thousands of jobs today.

"PILOTS SHOULD CARRY HANKERCHIEFS IN A HANDY POSITION TO WIPE OFF GOGGLES"

"RIDING ON THE STEPS, WINGS OR TAIL OF A MACHINE IN FLIGHT IS PROHIBITED"

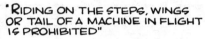

THE *ONLY* WAY TO FLY!

"IF YOU SEE ANOTHER MACHINE NEAR YOU, GET OUT OF ITS WAY"

MAKES SENSE!

"IF AN EMERGENCY OCCURS WHILE FLYING, LAND AS SOON AS YOU CAN"

NOW *THAT'S* ONE REG THAT'S PRETTY HARD TO IGNORE!

To all who have seen our nations outstanding air demonstration teams perform, one thing is very apparent — their absolute precision in everything they do. Now this precision business can be carried too far.

"There are no atheists in foxholes" goes an old expression. It applied equally to men in air combat. As a matter of fact, I doubt that you'd meet an atheist on the far side of the bomb line in *any* war.

Taking a young newly-minted and often intimidated aviator and molding him into a roaring tiger of a fighter jock takes a lot of patience, practice and prudence. Ask any RTU instructor (who still has all his marbles).

We've had an exchange pilot program between the armed services for many years. This story involves an Air Force blue suiter operating Navy machinery off the coast of Vietnam. The plane is a "SPAD," or Skyraider. There was also an Air Force version of the Skyraider, or AD-1.

AN AD-5 SKYRAIDER (AKA THE "SPAD") IS ON A CARRIER'S CATAPULT READY TO LAUNCH WITH A TRUCK LOAD OF STORES.

MEANS: "MY INSURANCE'S PAID UP, I THINK I'M READY TO GO."

A BROKEN CATAPULT YOKE - JUST A MINOR MALFUNCTION - LEAVES THE SPAD IN PLACE BUT CATCHES THE WOUND-UP PROP...

ROWR!

WHOOSH!

... and FLINGS THE R-3350 A COUPLE OF MILES OUT TO SEA

KA-FLANNG!

MEANS: "ON SECOND THOUGHT, CAN'T WE TALK THIS OVER?"

Let's stroll down the memory lane of aircraft microphones. I wish I could say, like the cigarette commercial, "You've come a long way. baby," but I really can't.

SOME SADIST DESIGNED A THROAT MIKE THAT WAS SUPPOSED TO FREE YOUR HANDS (BUT TO KEEP FROM CHOKING, YOU HAD TO LEAVE IT LOOSE & HOLD IT TO TALK ANYWAY).

I SAY AGAIN... AWK!

ZZZAP

(P.S. SWEAT "SHORTED 'EM OUT" and LEFT BURN MARKS ON YOUR NECK)

BRITISH WWII MODELS WERE IN A FABRIC FLAP WITH THE OXY MASK. THE PROTRUDING EAR-PHONES CAPPED THE PICTURE.

I SAY, YANK, LET'S GIVE 'ER A RUDDY GO!

WHERE IS THAT DAMN THING?

THEN THERE WERE THE CUMBERSOME HAND-HELD JOBS. GREAT WHEN ALONE, TRYING TO MAKE AN IFR AP-PROACH, LAP FULL OF MAPS, 3 GUYS TALKIN' AT YA, ETC., ETC.

FINALLY, WE PROGRESSED TO THE LIGHTWEIGHT LIP MIKE—WHICH YOU CAN ALWAYS EAT IN TENSE SITUATIONS –

WE JUST LOST NO. 4, TOO?

ULP!

NOTHING, BUT NOTHING, EVER BEAT THE HUMAN VOICE BOX WHEN IN A REAL JAM—

WHICH WAY TO IRELAND?

LINDBERGH IN "SPIRIT OF ST. LOUIS", N.Y. TO PARIS, 1927.

"If God had intended man to fly, He would have given him wings" — so goes an old saw which we might amend to: "If God had intended man to fly *instruments*, He would also have given him a built-in artificial horizon."

We continue with our treatise on instrument flying this month by demonstrating — via bird's eye view — the flight path of a typical C-47 practice GCA. (Ground Controlled Approach)

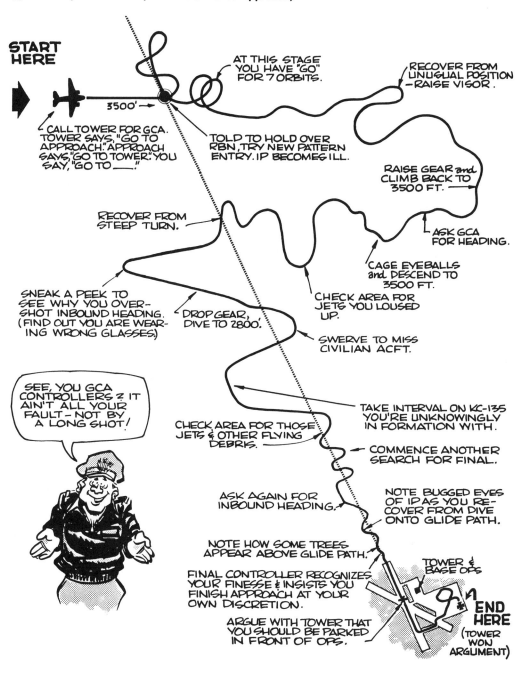

These stories were told to me by General Chuck Yeager. Many readers will recall that General Yeager was the first man to break the speed of sound back in the "good old days," 1947. He achieved this remarkable feat in the X-1, "Glamorous Glennis," a rocket ship which now hangs in the Smithsonian Institution.

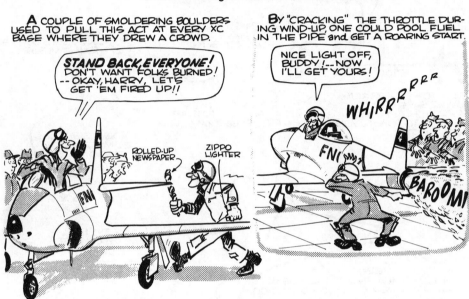

A COUPLE OF SMOLDERING BOULDERS USED TO PULL THIS ACT AT EVERY XC BASE WHERE THEY DREW A CROWD.

STAND BACK, EVERYONE! DON'T WANT FOLKS BURNED! --OKAY, HARRY, LET'S GET 'EM FIRED UP!!

ROLLED-UP NEWSPAPER

ZIPPO LIGHTER

BY "CRACKING" THE THROTTLE DURING WIND-UP, ONE COULD POOL FUEL IN THE PIPE AND GET A ROARING START.

NICE LIGHT OFF, BUDDY!--NOW I'LL GET YOURS!

WHIRRRRRR

BAROOM!

ANOTHER CLOWN-WHO SHALL REMAIN NAMELESS-USED TO BEAT UP REMOTE XC REFUELING STOPS and THEN...

WOW! LOOKIT THAT!! AN AIRPLANE WITH NO PROP! WONDER WHAT KINDA STRANGE BIRD FLIES THAT?

...AS THE TRANSIENT CREW VERY CAUTIOUSLY APPROACHED, HE'D SLIP A RUBBER HORROR MASK ON UNDER HIS P.1 HELMET—

GOT ANY JP-1, SONNY?

Let's take a look at our English cousins during "the big one." They had a vocabulary of flight that was unique and as far removed from ours as the United States was from jolly old. Pilot Officer Prune is our equivalent of Roger Rudder — a young, dashing fighter pilot.

"PILOT OFFICER PRUNE" – THE RAF EQUIVALENT OF ROGER RUDDER. WAS NORMALLY 19 YRS OLD WITH PIMPLES.

MOSS BROS. HAT (WITH 50* MISSION CRUSH)

TOP BUTTON UN-BUTTONED SIG-NIFIED "I'M A FIGHTER JOCK"

WHITE TURTLENECK SWEATER LIBERATED FROM DRUNKEN ROYAL NAVY SUBMARINER

CROP RIDING (RIDING _WHAT?_)

NO. 1 BLUES TUNIC

"BOWSER" – A GAS TRUCK (OR PETROL LORRY)

PANTS, TUCKED IN (_LOOSELY!_)

FUR-LINED FLYING BOOTS (TOPS TURNED DOWN)

"TANNOY" (LOUDSPEAKER) USUALLY MANNED BY SOME LAC (LEADING AIRCRAFTSMAN) WHO RETIRED TO THE SACK AFTER ROUSTING OUT ALL THE LADS.

OPS NO 12 SQUADRC

I SAY, SCRAMBLE NO. 12 SQ.!

WDOK

PILOT'S INITIALS

* ALTHOUGH HE HAD BARELY SURVIVED THREE "CIRCUITS-and-BUMPS" (TOUCH-and-GOES) IN A "HURRY" (HURRICANE)

WINDSCREEN

GOR BLIMEY!

PETROL TANKS

BARRAGE BALLOONS

AIRSCREW (NO KIDDIN'!)

ALIGHTING GEAR

This cartoon depicts the pre-takeoff briefing given to Rebel aviators at the 1966 Confederate Air Force show. It was dreamed up by that great humorist in the CAF ranks, Lloyd Nolan. Actually, the briefing and safety precautions are businesslike and detailed.

CONFEDERATE AIR FORCE

The following was written by a 5th grade student of Jefferson School, Beaufort, S.C. It was first published in the <u>South Carolina Aviation News</u>. We think it's a classic.

WHY I WANT TO BE A PILOT

WHEN I GROW UP I WANT TO BE A PILOT BECAUZE IT'S A FUN JOB AND EASY TO DO. THATS WHY THERE ARE SO MANY PILOTS FLYING AROUND THEZE DAYS.

PILOTS DONT NEED MUCH SCHOOL. THEY JUST HAVE TO LEARN TO READ NUMBERS SO THEY CAN READ THEIR INSTRUMENTS.

I GUESS THEY SHOULD BE ABLE TO READ A ROAD MAP, TOO...

PILOTS SHOULD BE BRAVE SO THEY WONT GET SCARED IF IT'S FOGGY AND THEY CAN'T SEE, OR IF A WING OR MOTOR FALLS OFF...

PILOTS HAVE TO HAVE GOOD EYES TO SEE THROUGH THE CLOUDS, AND THEY CANT BE AFRAID OF THUNDER OR LIGHTENING BECAUZE THEY ARE MUCH CLOSER TO THEM THAN WE ARE.

THE SALARY PILOTS MAKE IS ANOTHER THING I LIKE. THEY MAKE MORE MONEY THAN THEY KNOW WHAT TO DO WITH. THIS IS BECAUZE MOST PEOPLE THINK THAT FLYING A PLANE IS DANGEROUS, EXCEPT PILOTS DON'T BECAUZE THEY KNOW HOW EASY IT IS.

I HOPE I DONT GET AIR-SICK BE-CAUZE I GET CAR-SICK AND IF I GET AIR-SICK I COULDN'T BE A PILOT AND THEN I WOULD HAVE TO GO TO WORK.

This page is strictly a polyglot with an emphasis on feet — yes feet! In war, be it on the ground or in the air, the saying "Take care of your feet and they'll take care of you" applies. Here again you see the venerable P-38. It was drafty in that nose compartment and they never did get a heater that would keep you warm below the kneecaps.

IN THE P-38, ILL-FITTING NOSE COWLING (AROUND THE GUN PORTS) PRODUCED A SUB-ZERO CONDITION AT THE RUDDER PEDALS...

...WHILE IN THE P-51, STRADDLING THAT MONSTROUS V1710 ALLISON BROUGHT THE COCKPIT TEMP UP TO THAT OF BOILING WATER *

HERE'S A RED HOT FIGHTER PILOT FREEZING TO DEATH IN HIS BIRD!

BLOCKS OF ICE

GAD! MY THIRD CANTEEN OF WATER..AND THE RELIEF TUBE OUT-LETS PLUGGED!

* PARTICULARLY IN THE PACIFIC AREAS.

PORTRAIT OF A NOVICE PASSENGER WHO MISTOOK THE EARPLUG WAX HANDED OUT FOR A PIECE OF CHEWING GUM ?

THERE ARE FEW MEN STILL FLYING WHO RODE IN THE BEHEMOTH B-36D. THOSE WHO DID MAY REMEMBER THIS CLASSIC EXCHANGE BETWEEN AN IP & A PILOT ABOARD ONE OF THE *10* ENGINED AERIAL TITANS:

FEATHER SIX!

WHICH SIX?

Don't let the cute dialogue — ala first grade primer — turn you away from this funny true story. (Cartoonists have fits of being cute at times and this one just slipped out.)

FLY, DICK, FLY. SEE DICK FLY. SEE DICK MAKING LANDINGS AT AN AUX. FIELD. SEE DICK LAND GEAR UP!

SEE DICK LOOK AROUND. LOOK, DICK, LOOK. HEAR DICK'S THOUGHT WHEELS TURNING. THINK, DICK, THINK!...AHA!

HEAR DICK MAKING A RADIO CALL. CALL, DICK, CALL. HEAR MAIN BASE PANIC. PANIC, MAIN BASE, PANIC!

WATCH THE LARGE HAND MOVE 5 MARKS ON THE WATCH, ER, CLOCK

HEAR DICK SAVE HIS GLUTEUS MAXIMUS. GOOD SHOW, DICK, GOOD SHOW!

Continuing our hard-to-believe-but-true series, we turn now to one Bruce Carr, who became an American fighter ace. Bruce was doing a stint in the ETO when the following incident actually happened.

KNOCKED DOWN OVER DER VATERLAND, CARR WAS PROMPTLY SCARFED UP *and* INCARCERATED.

I DON'T THINK I'M GONNA LIKE THIS A-TALL!

BRUCE MADE REPEATED ATTEMPTS TO ALTER HIS SITUATION—

NOW I *KNOW* I DON'T LIKE BEIN' A KRIEGIE*

ZANG

ZIP

* P.O.W.

AFTER AN EXTENDED PERIOD, HE ESCAPED BY "BORROWING" AN ME-109 FROM THE FIRST AIRFIELD HE CAME TO...

...*and* THEN FLEW BACK TO HIS BASE IN THE U.K. THE A/A PEOPLE GAVE HIM AN APPROPRIATE WELCOME—

AFTER MAKING A BELLY LANDING, HE WAS PROMPTLY MET BY HIS C.O. (*and* OTHER INTERESTED PARTIES)

WHAT THE @∾!ö:*! DOES "AUSFAHRT" MEAN?

HOLD IT, YOU DUMMIES! IT'S *ME!* GAD WHERE'S THE GEAR LEVER?

CARR! WHERE IN HELL HAVE YOU BEEN?

MP.

NEXT: THE P-51 SHOT DOWN BY A *TANK!*

This one's hard to believe but the guy it happened to — Jim Croker, Oklahoma State Director of the Combat Pilots Association — has the scars (and the medals) to prove it. Jim has kept this little episode more or less a secret over many years for obvious reasons.

Many of our NATO allies took their early World War II training in the venerable Tiger Moth. These otherwise sturdy little birds had a penchant for shedding a wheel on takeoff — this, plus no radios aboard, made for some interesting stories.

AT A RNAF (ROYAL NETHERLANDS AF) TRAINING BASE —

OH OH! THAT'S A STUDENT!! WE'VE GOT TO WARN HIM!

TWO INSTRUCTORS GRAB A SPARE WHEEL and ANOTHER MOTH TO GIVE CHASE.

WE'LL HAVE TO SHOW HIM THE PROBLEM BEFORE HE TRIES TO LAND!

POP POP POP

WOULDN'T YA KNOW! THE INSTRUCTORS' BIRD SHEDS A WHEEL UNBEKNOWNST TO THEM —

FINALLY THEY CATCH THE STUDENT —

HEY! THAT'S A NEAT TRICK! I WONDER HOWINTHEHELL THEY DO THAT?

P.S. BOTH ACFT MADE REASONABLY UNEVENTFUL CRASH LANDINGS.

I fell heir to a batch of <u>YANK</u> magazines and <u>STARS AND STRIPES</u> papers. Thumbing through these treasures revealed our life and times back during "The Big One"...

OVERSEAS WE HAD:

THE SAD SACK

(GEO. BAKER)

Winnie the Wac*

(VIC HERMAN)
*and WAAFs, WRENS AWASS, AWALs, WENLs etc., etc.

3.2 BEER

(OZZIE ST. GEORGE)

ARMED FORCES RADIO

NEWCOMER CPL. JACK PAAR

KILROY WAS HERE
and (ANON)
SNAFU, TARFU, etc

PINUPS and NOSE ART

THE MOST FAMOUS OF ALL WW II PINUPS— BETTY GRABLE

(OH, THAT LUCKY HARRY JAMES!)

(P.S. ALL POSTER PILOTS LOOKED LIKE TYRONE POWER)

Elsie

(ALA PETTY)

SLOGANS: "REMEMBER PEARL HARBOR!"
"A-SLIP-OF-THE-LIP-CAN-SINK-A-SHIP!"
"BUNDLES FOR BRITAIN"
"When the lights go on again all over the world"

WHILE BACK HOME SOME OF THE 4Fers WORE "ZOOT SUITS" and OGLED OUR WOMEN...

WAR BONDS

JUST MEET THOSE SCHEDULES, WILL YOU?

"WINNIE"

ANDREWS SISTERS HAIRDO

7-FT KEY CHAIN

TO BE CONT.

It's nostalgia time again as we continue our "remember when?" ticklers that appeared on the previous page. We'll wrap it up with these goodies:

OVERSEAS WE HAD:

DINKY STOVES

TOKYO ROSE *
and (AXIS SALLY, TOO)

HERRO YANKEES

* THIS IS WHAT WE *THOUGHT* SHE LOOKED LIKE!

50 CAL.

BUTTS

DOG TAGS

DOE JOHN M
A074621A
T43 44 O P

RELIGION
BLOOD TYPE
INITIAL TETANUS SERIES
(ANYBODY KNOW WHY THEY WERE NOTCHED?)

GI SHOES

– FASHIONED FOR NORTH AFRICAN OR PACIFIC WEAR.

SANITATION FACILITIES
–AL FRESCO

AIRCRAFT RECOGNITION

FLASH QUICK! P-47 OR TOGO?

American energy will win!

AT HOME IT WAS RATIONING:

A GAS

MEAT, SUGAR, SHOES – YOU NAME IT – STAMPS

...and THE GALS TRIED TO LOOK LIKE VERONICA LAKE (WITH HER "PEEK-A-BOO" HAIR DO)

IKE and MAC

FINALLY – AFTER WHAT SEEMED LIKE EONS.

PARTICULARLY HARD TO GET WERE:
• HERSHEY BARS
• NEW TIRES
• NYLONS – WOMEN PAINTED THEIR LEGS INSTEAD
• and BOOZE!
"CANE NEUTRAL SPIRITS" WERE AVAILABLE, BUT IT'D BLOW A SAFE!

THEY EVEN PUT STRIPES DOWN THE BACK!

SCRAP DRIVES –
WITH SOME LOCAL POL PUNCHIN' THE AXIS...

EXTRA
VALLEY MORNING STAR
WAR IN PACIFIC OVER!

Flying around Muroc AAB (later to become Edwards AFB Flight Test Center) one could come across very strange flying machines in the '40s and '50s. As a matter of fact, you can still see some weird birds over that California lake bed...

The night fighter's lot was a lonely one — solitary birds stalking their prey in pitch-black conditions. Pilot and radio operator (RO) were an inseparable team both in the air and on the ground — *usually*. At the height of Air Defense Command's heyday, this event actually happened. If you've ever been awakened in the dead of night by a wailing claxon, you can understand how.

The P-38 was particularly vulnerable to zany ideas for new missions and armament because of its size, speed, and tremendous load-carrying ability. Did you ever think, "Who in the hell came up the *that* idea?". Usually it was some bushy brain in old five sides by the Potomac. Many times, however, these strokes of genius came from misguided souls in our midst — even down to the squadron level.

SCREWBALL IDEAS WE'D LIKE TO FORGET!

A POX ON THE GENIUS WHO EXCHANGED THE DROP TANK BUTTON ON THE CONTROL WHEEL FOR THE MIKE SWITCH

WE'D LIKE TO CATCH THE CLOWN WHO — IN THOSE EARLY & ELECTRONICALLY UNSOPHISTICATED DAYS — THOUGHT TAIL WARNING RADAR WOULD BE A GOOD THING ON FIGHTERS —

AND A FURLINED BARF BAG TO THE IDIOT WHO THOUGHT A CHECK-OUT RIDE SHOULD CONSIST OF STUFFING YOU INTO THE RADIO COMPARTMENT WHERE ALL YOU COULD SEE WAS THE PILOT'S NECK & ALL YOU SMELLED WAS 100/130 OCTANE —

MAY THE GUY WHO THOUGHT OF USING DROP TANKS AS PERSONNEL CARRIERS BE CONDEMNED TO RIDE THROUGH THE HEREAFTER IN ONE —

Here's a clutch of B-17 stories. The venerable "Fort" produced as many stories as bomb tonnage dropped... mainly because there were ten characters aboard each bird. Most of 'em were like those shown here:

Between the wars (any two since World War I will do), airfields normally saturated with traffic while the shooting was going on, tended to fade into obscurity. This story is about just such a place and was told to me by a Flying Tiger captain who's had some marvelous exchanges with towers worldwide.

Gunners have been a part of the military air combat crew since before WW I. Without 'em in WW II, the "Fort" and "Lib" would have been clay pigeons. Tons and tons of .50 cal. and 20mm ammo poured from their guns — and a lot of it actually hit the enemy! Today, their ranks thinned by technology, gunners still "hang tough" in venerable B-52.

This has to be the ultimate in foul-ups in communication. I'm indebted to the *TALON* — official cadet newspaper of the Air Academy — for this hilarious scenario. Only minds strained to the breaking point by the undergraduate study come up with a libretto like this one.

This story came from a Chinese National Air Cargo ex-Flying Tiger pilot. It's a true story about a C-46 driver and a check pilot in the days of CNAC's history of flying cargo around the Asian continent. The 'ol "Commando" was a sturdy bird, but it sure as hell didn't like to fly sideways.

CBI (CHINA-BURMA-INDIA) CHECK RIDE IN AN OL' C-46

SO THIS IS THE HOTSHOT WHO CAN CLEAN UP A SINGLE ENGINE IN 20 SECONDS. WELL, WE'LL JUST SEE...

TURNING OFF THE FUEL TO RIGHT ENGINE.

THEN, BEFORE THE ENGINE QUITS, THE CHECK PILOT STOMPS ON THE *LEFT* RUDDER!

ENGINE OUT! LET'S SEE YOUR ACT!

NOSE TURNING LEFT-ENGINE SPUTTERING... THIS IS CHILD'S PLAY...

THE CHECKEE STOMPS ON THE *RIGHT* RUDDER TO KEEP DIRECTIONAL CONTROL JUST AS THE MILL QUITS *and...*

SCRONK!

QUICKLY FEATHERS THE *LEFT* PROP!

LOUD SILENCE AIN'T IT?

We 5th Fighter Command troops liberated some pretty weird booze in the occupation of Japan. "Kamikaze juice" was a case in point. The setting for this story is true — the event... well, it *could* have happened.

SCENE: A LOCKED ROOM ON THE 10TH FLOOR OF A FUKUOKA HOTEL—

BUDDY, TRY SOME OF THIS. THEY GAVE IT TO THEIR SUICIDE PILOTS BEFORE THEIR LAST MISSION.

GEE, I DUNNO OLNEY...

(A HOUSE BRAND WHICH, UNBE- KNOWNST TO OUR HEROES, WAS LIBERALLY LACED WITH COCAINE)

THE TASTE TEST WAS GOING SWIMMINGLY WHEN THERE CAME...

OLNEY, OPEN THE ⓖ✱ⓛ☼ WINDOW—I'M GONNA FLY BACK TO THE BASE.

FLAP FLAP FLAP FLAP FLAP

A TAPPING AT THE DOOR—

BAM! BAM! BAM! OPEN UP IN THERE—MILITARY POLICE!

GERONIMOOO...

FUKUOKA HOTEL

...and WHEN YOU SAW HE WAS GOING TO JUMP, WHY DIDN'T YOU TRY TO STOP HIM?

BOARD OF INQUIRY

STOP HIM? HELL, I THOUGHT HE COULD *MAKE* IT... SIR!

During World War II, the AAF issued wings for just about any job that involved an aircraft. There were just about as many types of wings as there were jobs on the flight line. There was one common element about the issuance of wings to personnel — you had to fly in order to get a pair.

JUST SUPPOSE THEY DECIDED TO MAKE THE WINGS REFLECT THE JOB?

NEWLY-MINTED COPILOT

AIR LIFTER

STAND BOARD

HELICOPTER

FIGHTER PILOT

HEADQUARTERS

No story on aviation humor would be complete without at least a page or two of "famous last words" — such utterances as: "That engine sound rough? Nah, it's just blowin' its nose, pull the gear up!" or, "Nah, those are friendly fighters."

FAMOUS LAST WORDS

One of the things that could numb the old military air transport pilot with terror was to "get violated" by penetrating the air defense identification zone (ADIZ) at the wrong spot. Fighters policed this line, which runs completely around the United States, and would turn you in at the drop of a nautical mile.

WE JOIN THE CREW OF A C-124 ("OLD SHAKY") NEARING THE CONUS AFTER A LONG OVER-WATER HAUL-

FAA CONTROL, THIS IS RED DOG LEADER-UNIDENTIFIED ACFT IS C-124 TAIL NUMBER 2149...MATS 2149, YOU ARE 60 MILES SOUTH OF COURSE!

BORED 3RD PILOT

NAVIGATOR

EMERGENCY KIT RADIO

ROGER, RED DOG LEADER...

NAV! THERE'S A FIGHTER OUT HERE! WHAT'S GOIN' ON? ARE WE LOST?

AS THE NAVIGATOR CHURNS AROUND UNDER THE SIGN OF THE TWINS (PANIC & CONFUSION) THE '24 RACKS AROUND TO A NEW COURSE-

*G★! BROKE MY PENCIL! OUCH! DAMNED DIVIDERS! QUICK! WHERE'S MY SEXTANT? OMIGOD, THERE'S AN OVERCAST... MEBBE WE ARE LOST! ETC. ETC. ETC..

U.S. AIR FORCE

LATER-

ADMISSIONS

HE KEEPS BABBLIN' ABOUT LOST FIGHTER PILOTS, FAA RADAR, OPERATIONS, ADIZS, N'STUFF LIKE THAT...SIR!

We now leave the carefree, devil-may-care days of training and enter the operational unit. Don't be dismayed by the depiction of prop and jet jobs on the same page. We leap over the span of three wars in less than the margin width of this page.

Here we have a little bit of training in various stages of the flying career of a cadet. Advanced training is shown in the case of the poor instructor pilot who just led his first practice formation flight. Basic jet aerobatics were taught in the venerable T-33 — not a real barn burner when going straight up.

LET'S LOOK AT A TYPICAL "SUPERFORT" INSTRUCTOR PILOT DURING THE POSTWAR ERA.

BLUE 'C' CAP

AF ISSUE

OLD 8TH AF PATCH

WINGS OF FAME WITH NAME

R3350

1 OF 4 (BLACK PAINT)

RICOCHET ROCK STOPPER

SPOON and PENCILS

YELLOW PAINT (TO KEEP THE BLACK FROM SLIDING OFF)

SURVIVAL KNIFE, GUM & CANDY

GLOVES-WORN AROUND NAVY TYPES.

A2 FLIGHT JACKET (NEEDING OIL CHANGE)

GREY FLIGHT PAJAMAS

"BRAIN BAG" WITH E6B, REVISIONS TO DASH ONE (6 MOS OLD) WT. and BALANCE SLIPSTICK, PLOTTER, OUTDATED MAPS, and 3 DAYS LAUNDRY, DIRTY.

CIVILIAN BOOTS

B-29 TRADEMARK
MONEY, FRESH FRUIT.

NAVIGATOR TRAINEES APPROACH RIDE FM-5 (AEROBATIC FAMILIARZATION IN THE FIGHTER ENVIRONMENT) WITH ZEST and ENTHUSIASM! PICK OUT THE STUDENT WHO JUST HAD A LUNCH OF TACOS, BEANS, FOOT-LONG HOT DOG and FRIES—

BAG, BARF

T-37

THEY, THEY, THEY TRIED TO KILL ME...

...LED HIS FIRST CADET FORMATION PRACTICE FLIGHT...

THE T-BIRD DIDN'T HAVE THE THRUST-TO-WEIGHT OF AN F-15...

YAS! BUNIONHEAD! WHEN THE AIRSPEED READS "O" and THE SMOKE FROM THE TAILPIPE BLOWS BACK PAST THE CANOPY, WE'RE NOT GOIN' ANY HIGHER!

USAF

The Thunderbirds, our magnificent aerobatic air-borne drill team — started out as the Acrojets back in the late '40s flying P-80 jets. They've progressed steadily over the years to hotter and hotter flying machines. They currently fly the F-16.

TAKE OUR SUBJECT, FOR EXAMPLE — HE'S SEEING HIS FIRST DEMONSTRATION BY THE USAF THUNDERBIRDS ...

FORMATION ROLL ON TAKEOFF

DIAMOND LOOP

FOR ALL WHO HAVE SEEN THESE LADS PERFORM — YOU KNOW HOW TIGHTLY THEY HANG IN THERE ...

BON TON ROULLE

UNTIL THAT FINAL "BOMB BURST"

BY CRACKY! I *KNEW* IF THEY KEPT FOOLIN' AROUND WITH THAT DERN THING, THEY'D PULL IT APART!

Here we have bail-out stories from several wars — or somewhere in between. These are all allegedly true and, as we all know, truth is funnier than fiction.

OUR FIRST SUBJECT—A C-46 CREW CHIEF NAMED DON BUSSART—COULD SLEEP ANY-WHERE-ANYTIME. PARKED ON THE RAMP, HE'S SAWIN' LOGS WHILE ANOTHER BIRD RUNS UP ON THE NEXT PAD...

THE NEIGHBOR SHUTS DOWN—

SINCE WE'RE ON CONDITIONED REFLEXES, WWII CREWS GOT *THE WORD* EARLY ON—

LISSEN! IF I SAY 'BAIL-OUT', DON'T COME BACK WITH 'WHAT DID YOU SAY?' BECAUSE YOU'LL BE TALKIN' TO YOURSELF!

INSTRUCTORS ARE INSTRUCTORS TO THE END-EVEN WHEN THEY FOR-GET THEIR SEAT BELTS...

YA **STILL** CAN'T DO A DECENT SLOW ROLL!

Most of our AAF World War II fighters, with the notable exception of the P-47 and P-61, were powered by liquid-cooled, in-line engines. (If you think I'm going to get into the pros and cons of this decision, you're crazy.) There was one thing for sure about the in-line engines, when you were out of coolant — you were out of luck.

WHEN VARIOUS FIGHTER GROUPS MIXED IT UP WITH THE ENEMY OVER THE BOMBER STREAM —and ALL ON A COMMON FREQUENCY—MISTAKES WERE BOUND TO HAPPEN...

HELP! I'M HIT and LOSING COOLANT! WHAT'LL I DO?

CALM DOWN AN' FEATHER IT, BUDDY!

FEATHER IT, HELL! I'M IN A MUSTANG!

ONE WAY TO DETERMINE WHETHER THE PUDDLE UNDER YOUR BIRD WAS FUEL OR COOLANT— A MIXTURE OF ALCOHOL and WATER—WAS TO DIP A PINKIE IN and TASTE IT.

PORTRAIT OF A PILOT WITH A LEAKY COOLANT TANK

— ME WORRY?

Tooling around over hostile Vietnam as a Forward Air Controller (FAC) in a tail dragger Cessna O-1 at low altitude and low airspeed (about 120 knots with everything open but the tool box) could be fraught with anxiety. There were *some* lighter moments, though...

"Love is blind" the old saying goes. Pilots of WW II fighters viewed their brethren stuck in machines other than *their* particular steed of the moment as poor souls condemned to perdition!

P-47 "THUNDERBOLT" (ALIAS "THE JUG")

P-38 "LIGHTNING" (FAST, EXCEPT IN RATE-OF-ROLL)

P-40 "WARHAWK" (WITH BUILT-IN HEADWIND)

P-39 "AIRACOBRA" (REAL SNAKY WITH A FULL LOAD)

Here we go again with communications — and the lack thereof. We have enough trouble understanding each other in the same branch of service — mix a couple of branches and you've got *real* trouble...

A NAVY "EXCHANGE" TYPE AVIATOR IS RIDIN' RIGHT SEAT TO A BLUE SUIT-ER ABOUT TO LIFT OFF IN A C-7...

(REACHING FOR THE GEAR)

TO THE SWABBIE, THAT MEANS JUST ONE THING — SO HE CHOPS THE POWER!

ANOTHER CLASSIC FOUL-UP: A SUPER-SABRE'S COMIN' OFF A STRIKE IN 'NAM. A RATTLED PILOT THINKS HE'S HIT & CALLS ON GUARD (EMERGENCY) FOR SOMEONE TO LOOK HIM OVER—

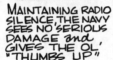

MAINTAINING RADIO SILENCE, THE NAVY SEES NO 'SERIOUS' DAMAGE *and* GIVES THE OL' "THUMBS UP"

Elsewhere in this issue the A-10 "Thunderbolt II" is compared with an earlier cannon-toting bird, the B-25G. The A-10, dubbed the Warthog (among other things) by its pilots, is an *ugly* — but exceedingly effective — weapon system.

THE "BIONIC TURTLE" IS SO UGLY PILOTS ON CROSS-COUNTRY FLIGHTS LAND AT OFF-THE-BEATEN-PATH AIRPORTS TO AVOID NASTY COMMENTS—

WHAT *IS* IT?

NEVER MIND! YA GOT ANY JP-4?

"THUNDER TURTLE" CREWMEN HAVE COME UP WITH THIS HIGHLY UNOFFICIAL INSIGNIA:

- SLOW, UGLY & PLODDING*
- NON-AERODYNAMIC
- HELPLESS ON ITS BACK
- HATCHED ON A REMOTE ISLAND
- PREDATES PRESENT TECHNOLOGY
- RETRACTS LEGS WITH TOES PROTRUDING

- BOXY WITH TOUGH SHELL
- HARD & DEADLY BITE
- LAYS A GREAT NO. OF EGGS
- TENACIOUS WITH STAYING POWER
- DIVES FOR ITS PREY
- EMERGES FROM ATTACK COVERED WITH MUCK

*SO SLOW IT GETS BIRD STRIKES FROM THE REAR!

WHEN THE BARN-DOOR DIVE BRAKES ARE OPENED, "SLAT" (Slow Low Airborne Target) PILOTS EXPERIENCE A REAL SENSATION—

ACME TRANSIT MIX

OMIGOSH! I'VE FLAMED OUT!

US AIR FORCE

THE BIRD IS A CREWMAN'S DREAM! *EVERYTHING* OPENS UP, and TURN-AROUND TIMES ARE THE FASTEST THING ABOUT THE A-10.

JUST A FEW MINOR GIGS... WE'LL HAVE HER READY IN 30 MIN., SIR!

(FROM CREWMAN'S FTD GRADUATION CERTIFICATE)

In days of yore we towed our own aerial gunnery targets with tactical aircraft for our squadron shootouts... It was a hairy job not made any easier by primitive tow gear. You became a tow pilot by drawing the short straw.

As tow pilot, hunkering down behind the armor plate afforded some psychological protection,

ZAP. ZING ZANG ZIP

GAD! THOSE ARE COMIN' CLOSE!

BLUE 3, COMIN' IN

LISSEN, YOU CLOWNS, I'M *PULLIN'* THIS THING — NOT PUSHIN' IT!

Now that air-to-air weapons and aircraft are more sophisticated, consider the following scenario:

BAD GUY

GOOD GUY (IN VTOL ACFT)

SPLASH!

"Where are we? I'm the navigator, I have a right to know!" Navigators have been the butt of many an aircrew's joke — however, *sometimes* they have the last word...

Few things in military life evoke more emotion than promotion lists. If you make one, particularly below the zone, its the highest of highs. If you miss your *second* go-around, well…

WE UNDERSTAND THE B-29 JOCK WHO PULLED THIS MANEUVER IN '45 WAS PASSED OVER … *and* OUT!

This issue we present a gallery of trivia about little-known U.S. fighters of WW II. You'll see why you haven't heard much about these outcasts when you meet:

THE VULTEE VANGUARD 48C

WAS BUILT FOR SWEDEN (WHICH PRU-DENTLY REFUSED TO ACCEPT THEM). THE USAAF KEPT THESE ORPHANS (AS THE P-66), FINALLY *GIVING* THE BIRD TO THE CHINESE. THERE, U.S. "VOLUNTEERS" FLEW 'EM.

THE BREWSTER "BUFFALO"

MODEL 339. LOOKED LIKE ONE; FAT, SHORT *and* UGLY. THEY FLEW LIKE THE SIDE OF A SCREEN PORCH. BUILT FOR THE NAVY, THEY WERE PALM-ED OFF ON THE RAF WHERE, AGAIN, AMERICANS HAD TO FLY THE BEASTS IN S.E. ASIA.

(THE TAIL WAS USED FOR THE BT-13 "VULTEE VIBRATOR" TRAINER)

THE NA-50

WAS BUILT FOR THAILAND. AGAIN, TAKEN OVER BY THE US *and* DUBBED THE P-64, WE USED THE DESIGN FOR THE VENERABLE T-6 TRAINER—

THE LIGHTNING I,

YP-38 ("YIPPEE") NONTURBO VERSION. 150 OF THESE CLUNKERS WENT TO ENGLAND. WITH EVERYTHING OPEN BUT THE TOOL BOX, THEY'D BARELY MAKE 16,000'. THE BRITISH GAVE 'EM BACK *and* WE USED 'EM TO TRAIN CADETS.*

* INCLUDING YOURS TRULY

The story of the Gooney birds of Midway Island is legend and long overdue for exposure in this space. The venerable C-47 got its name from these prolific feathered clowns — their flight characteristics were similar.

Instrument training is a *real* pain — particularly when it's hot, the hood doesn't fit right, the air's bumpy and you're involved in the ultimate exercise of boredom — holding patterns.

A C-45 CREW IS STACKED IN A PATTERN NEAR THE TOP—THE WEATHER'S CLEAR.

2107, YOU ARE NOW CLEARED TO 7000. REPORT LEAVING EIGHT.

107, ROGER OUTTA 8 FOR 7.

GAD! AM I EVER POOPED. THIS IS TAKIN' FOREVER TO GET DOWN!

YEH, and LOOK AT THOSE FUEL GAUGES. WE'RE GETTIN' LOW!

DISCRETION BEING THE BETTER PART OF VALOR, 107 PULLS OUT, DESCENDS, and LANDS VFR.

Z

YAWN!

JACK, YOU STAY ON APPROACH, I'M GOIN' TO TOWER.

AND WHILE THE CO-PILOT STAYS ON THE HORN & GIVES THE APPROPRIATE ANSWERS TO APPROACH, THEY LOAD UP WITH FUEL & COKES...

2107, YOU ARE NOW CLEARED TO 4 THOUSAND.

ROG, LEAVIN' FIVE.

100 OCT.

REFRESHED and RE-FUELED, THEY TAKE OFF, RE-ENTER THE STACK JUST IN TIME TO HEAR:

2107, YOU ARE NOW CLEARED FOR YOUR FINAL APPROACH.

BE MY GUEST

If you've ever had someone horn into line ahead of you while awaiting takeoff clearance, you'll appreciate this story. The setting was an air base shared by the old B-25s and the then-new B-47 medium bombers...

Air traffic controllers can be a rather detached lot — especially when you're slopping about in the soup several miles above them (after all, the furthest *they* can fall is off their chairs).

THIS LITTLE STORY INVOLVES A TACITURN BRITISH TOWER CONTROLLER and A YANK TRYING TO FIND OUT WHAT IT'S LIKE DOWN THERE—

DUXFORD TOWER, THIS IS BLINDMAN BLUE 2—WHAT'S YOUR WEATHER LIKE?

LOOKS *FIT*, OLD BOY.

SIGH

OKAY, THEN WHAT ARE YOUR WINDS?

I'D SAY *COOL*, OL'CHAP.

THANKS TO M/GEN FRED HAEFFNER

TRAFFIC WATCH *

AIR FORCE 1234, YOU HAVE TRAFFIC AT TWO O'CLOCK, 6 MILES...

CONTROL, CAN YA GIVE US ANOTHER CLUE? WE'VE GOT DIGITAL WATCHES

Nostalgia Quiz Corner

WHAT DID THIS MEMORY PHRASE MEAN IN WWII TRAINING?

"WHEN UNDERTAKING VERY HARD ROUTES KEEP DIRECTIONS BY VERY GOOD METHODS"

answer
THE FIRST LETTERS WERE MORSE CODE IDENTIFIERS FOR US AIRWAY "LIGHT LINE" BEACONS USED FOR NIGHT PILOTAGE. THE LINE STARTED WITH W.

Southeast Asia's nightmare often gave participants a feeling
of being caught in a time warp. Consider the crew that met an
intruder-type B-26 (originally the Douglas A-26, circa 1944)
which diverted to their F-4 base one night…

They were called "little tin guys" (for what reason I haven't the foggiest notion) — however, navigators were made of the same stuff as other aircrewmen. In the days before Loran and Inertial Guidance, a lot hung on the bubble in their octant —

1500 MILES OF WATER OUT → ← and BACK!

"He that is down need fear no fall"
                        Bunyan
This page is dedicated to all of us who've had those days when we
"shoulda stayed in bed" as Murphy's law took over.

YOU *KNOW* IT'S NOT YOUR DAY WHEN...

... RETURNING FROM A MISSION YOU WALK INTO SQUADRON OPS and SEE THE EJECTION SEAT PINS— COMPLETE WITH STREAMERS—IN YOUR POCKET!

...YOU PULL UP OFF A BOMB RANGE PASS TO FIND ONE OF YOUR 500 POUNDERS FLYING CLOSE FORMATION WITH YOU!

...YOU REACH FOR THE "FLAP" RETRACT LEVER ON LANDING and GET THAT SINKING FEEL- ING, LITERALLY and FIGURATIVELY!

...TAXIING OFF THE RUN- WAY AFTER LANDING YOU TAXI INTO THE GRASS WHILE FILLING OUT THE AIRCRAFT FORMS—

It's potpourri time again — here is a sampler of vignettes from various time and various places. No big theme or message — enjoy!

The flying saucer/UFO mania (AKA "Project Bluebook") was at virulent level in the mid-'50s. From our dusty archives, we dug out this story about a contractor crew delivering a EC-121 to Edwards AFB for testing...

Good wingmen who "hang in there" when the goin' gets tough are essential to air combat. There is also a time-honored tradition that good wingmen keep their radio transmissions to a minimum.

One job we've never touched on in this space is the role the combat photographer played in WW II. These stalwart souls risked life and limb to tell it like it was! (If you think I'm trying to make brownie points with our C in C — who was in the 1st Motion Picture unit — yer right!)

Now that women pilots are coming out of the ATC pipeline — including the halls of the USAF Academy — military flying stories have and added dimension (ladies, that statement does not necessarily mean *width*, either!)

The armada-style WW II bomber raids over Europe were awesome in size, destruction and losses. There has been a lot of somber newsprint, and rightfully so, about places like Schweinfurt, Ploesti, Berlin, et al., but there were some lighter moments, too...

Back in "the big one", the U.S. Army Air Forces, née Air Corps, trained a lot of Chinese cadets (there was just *one* China). To say there was a communications gap would be the understatement of the age!

We present herewith some of the trivia that collected in the backwash of WW II. These anecdotes, and other minutiae, kept up busy in the telling and retelling (hell, you could even get an argument started over where the walls stopped and the ceiling began on a Nissen Hut!)

HEAR ABOUT THE CLOWN WHO ACCIDENTAL-LY USED 100 OCT. AVGAS INSTEAD OF KERO-SENE IN THE GP. LATRINE? AN INNOCENT BYSITTER SINGED HIS GLUTEUS MAXIMUS TOSSING A BUTT DOWN—

NISSEN HUT→

SIGN IN A PUB NEAR AN AAF BASE IN ENGLAND

IF YOU THINK OUR BAR-MAID IS BEAUTIFUL —DON'T DRIVE HOME
The Mgr—

REMEMBER **KILROY?** THE ADJ. GEN's OFFICE STIFFLY ANNOUNCED 27 SEP 1946 THAT HE WAS A "MYTHICAL FIGURE" (ACTUALLY, THERE WERE 62 KILROYS OUT OF 12 MILLION G.I.s IN WW II).

NO GRASS ATOLL
NO TREES ATOLL
NO WATER ATOLL
NO WOMEN ATOLL
NO LIQUOR ATOLL
NO FUN ATOLL
and NO KILROY ATOLL!

I JUST DIDN'T PAUSE ATOLL KILROY

KWAJALEIN ATOLL OPS

P.S. FRANCIS J. (FRANK) KILROY, JR., 461st BG, 15AF, CLAIMS TO HAVE STARTED IT ALL AT BOCA RATON IN 1943!

WHAT WAS A "MICKEY MAN"?

Ans: He operated a "Mickey Set," of course! Actually, a radar spe-cialist working amidships in a B-17.

The airman's mind in repose (a state of limbo during the hours & hours of boredom between moments of stark terror associated with combat) can conjure up some weird nicknames for men and equipment. Here's some oldies from our time in pinks & greens (or blues — depending on your D.O.B.)...

THE UC-78, CESSNA "BOBCAT"— A WOOD and FABRIC *ADVANCED* TRAINER WAS ALSO KNOWN AS:

FIXED-PITCH *WOOD* PROPS

" THE BAMBOO BOMBER"
" DOUBLE-BREASTED CUB"
" RHAPSODY IN GLUE"
" SAN JOAQUIN BEAUFIGHTER"
" FAMILY CAR OF THE AIR"

THE WARRANT OFFICER, OR "HALF LT.," DREW A LOT OF FLAK...

CAP INSIGNIA WAS CALLED "THE STALLED-OUT DUCK"

SMALLER DUCK INSIGNIA HERE ON EARLY MODELS

"BLUE PICKLE" BARS

(THERE WERE JR. and SR. GRADES)

HERE'S A FEW LATER MONIKERS:

IT ALL STARTED WITH THE PHANTOM. YOU *HAD* TO HAVE A NAME FOR THAT GUY IN THE OTHER SEAT!

F-4 = **GIB** (SIMPLY, <u>G</u>UY <u>I</u>N <u>B</u>ACK)

F-105 F/G = **BEAR** (HE'S IN HIS PIT)

F-111 = **YOT** ("YOU OVER THERE!")
note: side by side seating

IT NEVER FAILS
YOU'VE HAD A FIELD DAY ON THE OTHER SIDE OF THE BOMB LINE ALONE & ARE SURE YOU GOT 2 CONFIRMED and 1 PROBABLE ONLY TO FIND ON YOUR RETURN THAT THE TAPE WAS NOT RE-MOVED FROM THE GUN CAMERA!

"Necessity is the mother of invention — an old saw — but true! The GI crew chief in a forward combat area *had* to be innovative to survive... parts were scarce. There were, however, the inevitable backfires.

A GOON, MINUS A STARTER, COULD BE STARTED BY A JEEP! WITNESS:

COL. ROY MILLER
SHREVEPORT, LA.

THERE WAS, HOWEVER, THE POSSIBILITY THE OL' P and W WOULD CATCH EARLY and REWIND THE STRING —

SOME ENGINEERING TYPE UP IN AIR COMMAND GP. HQ. (BURMA) THOUGHT THE LITTLE LIAISON BIRDS SHOULD HAVE A WAY TO STRIKE BACK...

FABRIC COVERED VULTEE L-5

THE RESULT WAS PREDICTABLE

Everything nowadays is miniaturized, computerized, motorized & homogenized. Little is left to the pilot but to ensure he's got the right software plugged into the correct hardware. What ever happened to the 'ol, "kick the tire, light the fire, and brief on guard" type pilotage?

Look-alikes in a war can cause a *lot* of trouble! Often it was shoot first, *then* identify. The fact that good designs, particularly fighter aircraft, were copied by the good guys and bad guys alike, didn't help things a bit, either!

IN THE PACIFIC IT WAS THE JAPANESE KI-44 "TOJO" THAT GAVE THE P-47 JUG PILOTS FITS—

ANY JUGS IN THAT FORMATION OVER IE SHIMA BETTER ROCK YOUR WINGS, *NOW!*

ANOTHER DOUBLE WAS THE KI-61 "TONY" & THE P-51.

HEH, HEH 2 MORE AN' I'M AN ACE!

FLIGHT OF TONYS

TACKED ON AS TAIL-END CHARLIE

P.S. IT HAPPENED! THE PILOT: WM A. SHOMO, 5TH AF FROM JEANNETTE, PENNA.

IN THE ETO, THE SPITFIRE and ME-109 WERE DEAD RINGERS FROM BEHIND—

DON'T *SHOOT,* YOU RUDDY FOOL! I'M YOUR WINGMAN!!

THE ITALIAN MACCHI C.202 and EARLY MUSTANGS (P-51A, B) COULD HAVE BEEN TWINS—

S'CUSA, COL. COMMANDANTE, WHEN I JOIN UPPA WITH MY FLIGHT... THEY ALL GOTTA WRONG MARKINGS!

OURSA THEIRSA

There's a "dirty tricks" department in the USAF, too. Pilots of two-place machines form the nucleus of this group. The modus operandi varies from bird to bird, but for sheer inventiveness you couldn't beat the T-33!

SET-UP: GIB (GUY IN BACK) IS FLYING. FAST LETDOWN.

WHEN GIF (GUY IN FRONT) BENDS DOWN, GIB PULLS MAX Gs...

ANOTHER GAMBIT WAS TO TURN THE TEMP. CONTROL TO FULL COLD (WHICH PRODUCED SNOW ON MOIST DAYS) and WITH THE CORRECT TIMING—

AND FOR GETTIN' ATTENTION-PLUS SCARIN' THE SOCKS OFF THE GIF - PAPER AIRPLANES MADE OUT OF OLD FORM 21As DID THE TRICK!

Research and Development! The words conjure up visions of weird things going on behind locked doors, under tarps, or in remote desert dry lakes! Kelly Johnson's "Skunk Works", Wright-Pat, and Edwards AFB come to mind. Here are a few R&D X-rated machines that are probably best forgotten:

XP-54: "SWOOSE-GOOSE" HIGH-ALT. FIGHTER ORDERED IN 1941, DID NOT APPEAR (1 ea.) UNTIL 1944.

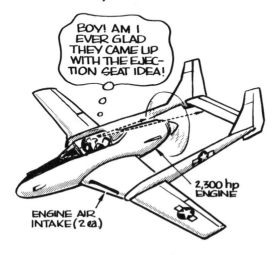

BOY! AM I EVER GLAD THEY CAME UP WITH THE EJEC-TION SEAT IDEA!

2,300 hp ENGINE

ENGINE AIR INTAKE (2 ea.)

XP-77: METAL WAS SCARCE IN WWII WHEN THIS LITTLE PLYWOOD FIGHTER APPEARED.

I HEAR TERMITES!

INVERTED IN-LINE ENGINE

NOT ALL WEIRDOS WERE IN THE FIGHTER RANKS. THE **XB-42** "MIXMASTER" HAD A TOTAL OF *TEN* PROP SHAFTS TO DRIVE THE CONTRA-ROTATING PROPS IN THE TAIL!

STOP CALLIN' ME FROG EYE!

2 'BLISTERS'

TRAINING WHEEL

THE **XB-53** (1948) WAS SUPPOSED TO HIT 583 mph – IT NEVER LEFT THE DRAWING BOARD.

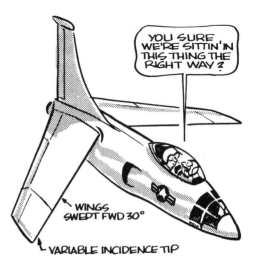

YOU SURE WE'RE SITTIN' IN THIS THING THE RIGHT WAY?

WINGS SWEPT FWD 30°

VARIABLE INCIDENCE TIP

Some time ago we ran a couple of episodes called "Gefractured German für fliegers". After a hiatus of more than two years a gifted gefractured writer surfaced in Canada — of all places. We think you'll like Fred Hicks' (of Winnipeg, Man.) gestorytellen…

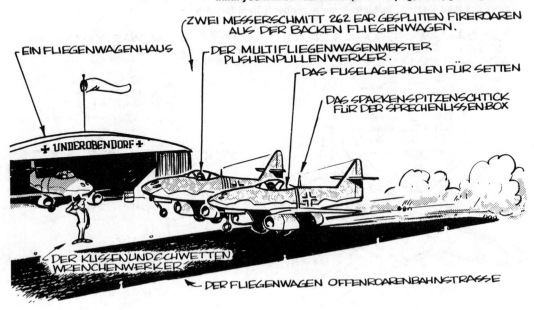

EIN FLIEGENWAGENHAUS

ZWEI MESSERSCHMITT 262 EAR GESPLITTEN FIREROAREN AUS DER BACKEN FLIEGENWAGEN.

DER MULTIFLIEGENWAGENMEISTER PUSHENPULLENWERKER.

DAS FUSELAGERHOLEN FÜR SETTEN

DAS SPARKENSPITZENSCHTICK FÜR DER SPRECHENLISSENBOX

+ UNDEROBENDORF +

DER KUSSENUNDECHWETTEN WRENCHENWERKER

DER FLIEGENWAGEN OFFENROARENBAHNSTRASSE

DAS WETTER

DER GROUNDENPOUNDER GESTORYTELLEN TIME —

DER KINDERGARTENER FLIEGENWAGEN

DER STUDENTEN ZOOMERLOOPENUNDGESTALLEN PUSHENPULLENWERKER.

DAS IST ALLES —

Since this issue deals with the USAF in space, we thought missiles would be a good subject... After all, what else can you put into space that isn't illegal?

SCENE: A TITAN II ICBM LAUNCH FACILITY SOMEWHERE IN KANSAS—

WE HAVE A FIRE IN THE LAUNCH DUCT!

QUICK! PREPARE TO LAUNCH THE BIRD!!

LAUNCH IT? IT'S PROBABLY GOIN' TO BLOW, SIR!!

RIGHT! AN' I'D RATHER NOT HAVE IT IN KANSAS WHEN IT DOES!

Aviation cadets have traditionally been on the receiving end of a lot of abuse from their instructors (the gosport only worked in one direction). Here's a true story about one cadet who struck back...

I *know* this is a true story for a couple of reasons: (1) My sainted mother asked the same questions of me, and (2) Col. "Turk" Moore, Jr. (who shared a miserable rock with me in the Pacific) says it also happened to him while home on leave.

Ever since Lt. Crissy dropped a hand-held bomb from a Wright Type B in 1911, people have been throwing things out of aircraft (primarily to do bodily harm to those below). Here are a few stories we hope won't "Bomb Out" —

Snappy retorts is the subject. How many times have you ever thought, "Gee, I wish *I'd* said that!" Usually the inspired reply comes to you a day or so after you've been zapped — or at 3 AM on a wakeful night. Here's some spur-of-the-moment deathless prose:

IT IS REPORTED THAT OL' LONESOME GEORGE GOBEL CAME UP WITH THIS BEAUT AFTER A TAXI ALTERCATION —

THEN THERE WAS THE 2ND LT. WHO WAS ON THE RECEIVING END OF A 20-MIN. TIRADE —

FINALLY, USING THE WRITTEN WORD, A LATRINE HUMORIST GOT IN THE LAST WORD IN THE MEN'S ROOM, BASE OPS, LOWRY AFB, COLO

* TOTAL MONTHLY CADET PAY-1943

Here's a classic. These sentiments, expressed by the 2nd in command of a Douglas racer roaring along at 180 mph, are still valid today. This poem had appeared in various forms and in countless publications; we liked this one —

THE CO-PILOT

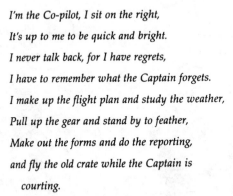

I'm the Co-pilot, I sit on the right,
It's up to me to be quick and bright.
I never talk back, for I have regrets,
I have to remember what the Captain forgets.
I make up the flight plan and study the weather,
Pull up the gear and stand by to feather,
Make out the forms and do the reporting,
and fly the old crate while the Captain is
   courting.

I take the readings and adjust the power,
Put on the heaters when we're in a shower,
I give him his bearings on the darkest of nights,
And do all the bookwork without any lights.
I call for my Captain and buy him a Coke,
And I always laugh at his corniest joke,
And once in a while, when his landings are rusty,
I always come through with "By gosh, but it's
   gusty!"

So all in all, I'm a general stooge
As I sit on the right of the man I call "Scrooge";
I suppose you think that is past understanding,
But maybe some day he'll give me a landing.

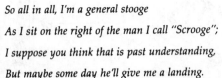

Your author recently flew his little private bird to Texas for the big Confederate Air Force show. Enroute we chanced to R.O.N. at Laughlin AFB, Del Rio (ATC). Col. "Bud" Farrington and his DO, Col. "Bunky" Reeves, made us feel downright welcome —

Early every October, the Confederate Air Force fights the major air battles of WW II over Rebel Field, Harlingen, Texas. The machines are authentic — foreign & domestic — and the action really grabs you! Tens of thousands of spectators thrill to "The Ghost Squadron" — a proud heritage of the air. The CAF moved to Midland-Odessa, Texas, in 1991.

ONE SCENARIO OPENS WITH THE ATTACK ON PEARL HARBOR. THE "TORA, TORA, TORA" GANG MAKES LIFE MISERABLE FOR THE B-17's P-40's and WILDCATS.

AW, C'MON, JETHRO, IT AIN'T *THAT* AUTHENTIC!

ヒコキ野郎!

REAL CRIPPLED B-17

REAL EXPLOSIVES

REAL SCARED

ANOTHER OPENING RECREATES THE BATTLE OF BRITAIN WITH *REAL* SPITS, ME-109's and HEINKELS!

GIVE 'IM A RUDDY BLAST, MATE!

P.S. SCORES OF BRITISH VISITORS THRILLED TO THIS and CHURCHILL'S BOOMING VOICE"... MEN WILL STILL SAY: THIS WAS THEIR FINEST HOUR."

THE FAA KEEPS A STRICT WATCH ON THE PROCEEDINGS — HOWEVER, A CAF BRIEFING IS JUST THAT — *BRIEF!*

NOW Y'ALL STAY ABOVE 5 FEET — AN' DON'T DO NOTHIN' DUMB!

THE BOMBERS ARE THERE, TOO, — *FLYIN'!* FOLLOW THE NUMBERS: 17, 23, 24, 25, 26 and THE '29!

"FIFI"

AS THE SHOW ENDS WITH CLOUDS OF SMOKE OVER JAPAN, A MISSING MAN FORMATION REMINDS ALL THAT WE, and FUTURE GENERATIONS, SHOULD BE PROUD OF THIS NATION'S ACCOMPLISHMENTS. THESE PLANES — and THE MEMORY OF THOSE WHO FLEW THEM — MUST BE PRESERVED!

"ETERNAL VIGILANCE IS THE PRICE OF LIBERTY",,, Thomas Jefferson

Weather forecasting is a black art. Men peer into radar screens and twirl knobs. Balloons ascend, satellites beam back code groups, anemometers spin, psychrometers whirl, and maps spew from the computers. With *all* of this, if they hit it right 50% of the time, they've whipped the odds!

In the soft-helmet era, all fighter groups used aircraft maneuvers plus head and hand signals to communicate while maintaining radio silence. Variations of this system are in use today. However, any time "body English" is used you'll run across someone who doesn't speak English…and that's the basis of this mini-series.

COMMUNICATING WITHOUT TALKING, PT I.

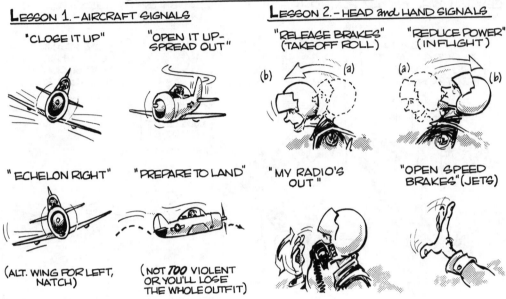

LESSON 1. – AIRCRAFT SIGNALS

"CLOSE IT UP"

"OPEN IT UP-SPREAD OUT"

"ECHELON RIGHT"

(ALT. WING FOR LEFT, NATCH)

"PREPARE TO LAND"

(NOT *TOO* VIOLENT OR YOU'LL LOSE THE WHOLE OUTFIT)

LESSON 2. – HEAD and HAND SIGNALS

"RELEASE BRAKES" (TAKEOFF ROLL)

"REDUCE POWER" (IN FLIGHT)

"MY RADIO'S OUT"

"OPEN SPEED BRAKES" (JETS)

REMEMBER "RELEASE BRAKES" SHOWN ABOVE? PICTURE 2 F-80s LINED UP (WITHOUT WINGTIP CLEARANCE) FOR TAKEOFF – THE LEADER SNEEZES...

AAH-

GO FOR IT, LEAD!

CHOO!

! PRANG!

ROAR

BRAKES STILL SET →

TO BE CONTINUED –

In our last episode we learned how fighter pilots signal to one another in silence using body and aircraft movements. The following true story is a perfect example of Murphy's Law in action. Only the aircraft flown and names have been changed to protect the innocent —

COMMUNICATING WITHOUT TALKING, PT. II

LARGE LOOSE FORMATION OF F-86s MAINTAINING RADIO SILENCE. LEAD SIGNALS TO WINGMAN —

"YOU TAKE LEAD — LET'S LAND"

WING TAKES LEAD, SIGNALS, "SPEED BRAKES OUT" (PREP FOR LETDOWN). FORMER LEAD ZIPS BACK INTO LEAD, SPEED BRAKES IN.

ZIP

?

LEAD HAS ELECTRICAL GLITCH; NO RADIO, NO FLAPS, NO NUTHIN'!

THIS AERIAL ALPHONSE and GASTON ACT TAKES PLACE SEVERAL TIMES BEFORE THE C.O. — WATCHING THINGS FROM THE REAR — FIRES OFF:

BLINDMAN TWO. WHAT'S WRONG WITH LEAD?

ZIP

BEATS ME, COL.!! THE SUM' BITCH DON'T WANNA STAY *UP* and HE DON'T WANNA GO *DOWN!*

At the risk of stepping on a few "Project Blue Book" toes, We're going to take up the subject of UFO's (Unidentified Flying Objects). A rash of sightings broke out in the early '50s & reached epidemic proportions when the Ground Observer Corps was in full cry by the '60s.

ONE INCIDENT INVOLVED A B-52 ON A NIGHT REFUELING MISSION WHICH MISTAKENLY TRIED TO HOOK UP TO A PASSING COMMERCIAL AIRLINER—

M'GAWD CAPT! LOOKIT THAT *BIG* LIGHTED CIGAR!

THIS IS THE AIRCRAFT COMMANDER— IF *ANY* OF YOU CLODS OPEN YOUR YAPS ABOUT THIS---

F-86Ds SCRAMBLED AT WRIGHT-PAT FOR NIGHT INTERCEPT OF, SAY, THE MOON WOULD BECOME "TARGETS" TO KEEP THE GROUND OBSERVERS HAPPY.

HERE I AM FOLKS! FRESH FROM MARS— and THERE ARE MORE COMING!

FU 460

LANDING LIGHT CANTED DOWN 15°

YOURS TRULY WAS SCRAMBLED TWICE FOR UFOs ...

BLINDMAN BLUE THIS IS GAS BAG CONTROL— TARGET AT 12 O'CLOCK CLOBBER IT!

WX BALLOON

I CAN'T. IT'S GOVT. ISSUE!

...ANOTHER TIME OUR FLIGHT BECAME SEPARATED IN WEATHER—

THIS IS GASBAG... YOU'RE CLOSING ON THE BOGIE!

THAT YOU, HERBIE?

DON'T SHOOT! I'M YOUR WINGMAN!

'S TRUE!

It's grab bag time. No big message... just some flotsam and jetsam that drifted up from the ol' file drawer. Enjoy...

THE FRUSTRATION OF BEING A PRIMARY STUDENT WHILE SHARING A BASE WITH YOUR ADVANCED BRETHREN CAN BE OVERPOWERING AT TIMES—

LAUGHLIN TOWER, THIS IS TWEET 44, REQUEST PERMISSION TO GO SUPERSONIC!

SUPERSONIC T-38

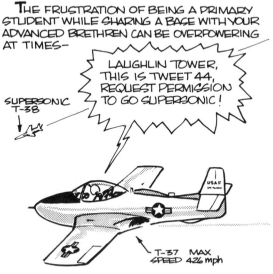

T-37 MAX SPEED 426 mph

390TH BG(H) REUNION DAYTON, O. JULY 20-24

ROGER, TWEET 44. USE LAUGHLIN 1 MOA. KEEP IT HIGH!

HEH HEH!

H'YAR AH GO... I

BOOM!

HERE'S A CLASSIC FROM A COPY OF WWII'S *YANK*—COURTESY OF THE LIBERATOR CLUB:

OH, WE RAN INTO *SOME* OPPOSITION ...

SAY "WHEN"

C-5

JET A

Both of these true stories occurred at Wright-Patterson AFB. Wright-Pat has had its share of weird and funny anecdotes — due primarily to the "cross roads" location and mission of the base. Light-years separate the two events.

BACK IN WWII, W-P WAS A FLIGHT TEST FACILITY. LOTS OF PUBLICITY SURROUNDED FLIGHTS OF NEW OR STRANGE AIRCRAFT—

CAPT. THIS IS A *REAL* THRILL FOR ALL OF US ON THE BASE! JUST HOW FAST IS THIS GERMAN JET?

CAPTURED Me-262

WELL, MA'AM, YOU KNOW A PILOT HAS TO FLY A MINIMUM OF 4 HOURS A MONTH TO GET HIS FLIGHT PAY; LI'L LADY, THIS BIRD IS SO FAST HE CAN EARN HIS FLIGHT PAY IN JUST 2 HRS!

AND, MORE RECENTLY, A HOTSHOT FIGHTER JOCK PASSIN' THROUGH BROUGHT HIS FAMILY OUT FOR THE PREFLIGHT RITUAL —

...THEN AFTER CHECKIN' THE WEATHER, FILIN' MY IFR FLT PLAN, WORKIN' OUT WT. and BALANCE, TAKEOFF DATA AN'...

G-SUIT, .38 CAL. PISTOL, FLIGHT BAG, ETC. ETC.

TECH DASH 1 AIM

HE BIDS HIS GRAND FAREWELL...

GOD SPEED, M'BOY.

SON, WITH ALL THOSE FUNNY CLOTHES ON, DON'T YOU THINK YOU SHOULD GO POTTY FIRST?

WAITING

MAJ. T. ARENZ

Recently this magazine ran a story which featured a column called,"You know you're overseas when…" this prompted the following from the Ex-CBI (China Burma India) *Roundup* from WW II.

" YOU KNOW YOU'RE A **REAL** CBIer WHEN YOU OPEN YOUR BEER CAN WITH A BAYONET… "

TROPICAL VERSION OF GI BROGANS

" REAL CBIers DON'T CALCULATE THE LOAD OF AN AIRPLANE. THEY EYEBALL THE CARGO *and* TAKE OFF WHEN THE PLANE LOOKS FULL"

" REAL CBIers WEAR JACKETS WITH STRANGE FLAGS *and* CRAZY WRITING ON THE BACK "

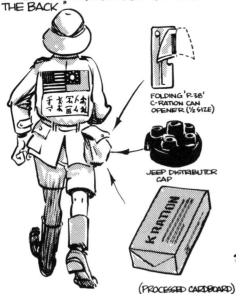

FOLDING 'P-38' C-RATION CAN OPENER (½ SIZE)

JEEP DISTRIBUTOR CAP

(PROCESSED CARDBOARD)

"REAL CBIers TRAVEL ANYWHERE IN THE WORLD FOR ANY LENGTH OF TIME WITH ONE BEAT-UP FLIGHT BAG" *

I THINK I CAN…I THINK I CAN… I THINK I C

* WITH SPACE, OF COURSE, FOR CAMEL CIGAR-ETTES, HERSHEY BARS & LADIES' SILK STOCKINGS!

Way back in 1975 we covered some regulations for operation of aircraft taken from a U.S. Air Service newsletter dated Jan. 1920. The following cogent points concerning landing taken from the same letter *still* make pretty good sense:

At Hill AFB, Ogden, Utah. One of AF Logistics Command's big CONUS centers, *everything* AFLC does contributes to the Air Force's combat capability — from putting the bubble in the navigator's sextant to overhauling a C-5. *BIG?* How does Hill's *6,666 acres under roof* grab you?

MAW (Military Airlift Wing). This is just one of MAC's 14 Z.I. bases. MAC is the backbone of the mobility for U.S. fighting forces & has nearly 150,000 people plus 1,400 aircraft to do the job — friends and enemies take note!

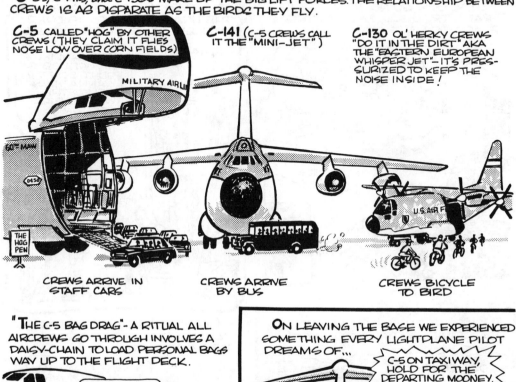

C-5s, C-141s, and C-130s MAKE UP THE BIG LIFT FORCES. THE RELATIONSHIP BETWEEN CREWS IS AS DISPARATE AS THE BIRDS THEY FLY.

C-5 CALLED "HOG" BY OTHER CREWS (THEY CLAIM IT FLIES NOSE LOW OVER CORN FIELDS)

C-141 (C-5 CREWS CALL IT THE "MINI-JET")

C-130 OL' HERKY CREWS "DO IT IN THE DIRT" AKA THE "EASTERN EUROPEAN WHISPER JET" — IT'S PRESSURIZED TO KEEP THE NOISE INSIDE!

CREWS ARRIVE IN STAFF CARS

CREWS ARRIVE BY BUS

CREWS BICYCLE TO BIRD

"THE C-5 BAG DRAG" - A RITUAL ALL AIRCREWS GO THROUGH INVOLVES A DAISY-CHAIN TO LOAD PERSONAL BAGS WAY UP TO THE FLIGHT DECK.

ON LEAVING THE BASE WE EXPERIENCED SOMETHING EVERY LIGHTPLANE PILOT DREAMS OF...

THIS GUY'S BAG BECOMES A WHEEL CHOCK NEXT TRIP!

P.S. IF THEY HADN'T HELD, BLOW WASH WOULD HAVE PUT US IN THE NEXT CO.!

Nellis AFB, Nevada is called "Home of the fighter pilot". This is TAC's fighter weapons center. Besides testing & evaluating Star Wars Weapons, combat-ready pilots hone their skills in such realistic conditions you expect to hear "Da and "Nyet" over the R/T! Oh, and the Thunderbirds nest here — a natural habitat!

WHILE IT'S TRUE TOWER OPERATORS TELL PILOTS WHERE TO GO, SOMETIMES THE ROLES ARE REVERSED—

There I Was... At the second busiest yet second smallest airfield in the Air Force! Thousands of cadets solo here each year. Fifty percent of the graduates are still on active duty! Know where? The U.S. Air Force Academy airfield.

THE PLACE IS HIGH - FIELD ELEV 7,200' (ON A HOT DAY, THE DENSITY ALTITUDE CAN REACH ALMOST 10,000 FT.!)

MR. STEVENS WANTS TO KNOW WHY WE DON'T ALLOW GO-AROUNDS ON THE GLIDER SIDE OF THE FIELD!

"GOAT SKINS" (FLYING SUITS) "ZOOMIE" AFA GRAD PILOT

SEVENTY PERCENT OF THE 4,000 CADETS SOLO OUT IN SOUPED-UP CESSNA T-41'S.

HOO BOY! JUST LIKE THE L.A. FREEWAY!

C'MON! LET'S KEEP THAT 30 SEC. SPACING!

SOF - SUPERVISOR OF FLYING SHACK (HEATED IN SUMMER. AIR COND. IN WINTER)

BESIDES FLYIN' THE '41s, THE 557 FTS HANDLES SOARING and MOTOR-GLIDER TRAINING—

NOW YOU KNOW WHY EVERYTHING IS PAINTED HIGH-VISIBILITY YELLOW.

THE "WINGS OF BLUE" TEAM and PARACHUTE COURSES SHARE THE SAME FIELD (SOARING & CHUTING ARE ELECTIVE; 60-70% OF THE CADETS SIGN UP).

IS THIS CONSIDERED A FLUNK, SIR?

All aircrews have their favorite stories, be they fighter, bomber, or transport types. We picked up these gems from a MAC crew beer-bust at Travis AFB a few months ago...

There I Was…Inside NORAD's Cheyenne Mt. Combat Ops Center in Colorado. This underground (9,500' of granite) city monitors surveillance data from all over the world to warn of an impending attack. NORAD's satellite and radar eyes all terminate here in this subterranean command post.

STEEL BLAST DOORS WEIGHING **25 TONS** _EACH_ STAND AT THE TUNNEL ENTRANCE.

LOOKS LIKE THE FRONT DOOR OF A NEW YORK WALK-UP FLAT.

A _MILLION_ POUNDS OF EXPLOSIVES WERE USED TO BLAST OUT NEARLY 3 MI. OF TUNNEL & CHAMBER SPACE!

YOU FELLERS SURE ARE MAKIN' A LOT OF NOISE OUT HERE!

THE CHEYENNE MT. YACHT CLUB PATROLS THE 4 WATER RESERVOIRS INSIDE THE MOUNTAIN—

BEATS ME—IT WASN'T HERE YESTERDAY...

B.S. WORD SMITH

(P.S. AN AIRMAN RECENTLY RE-UPPED ABOARD THE WORD SMITH!)

IN THE MISSILE WARNING CENTER AN ACCURATE TAB IS KEPT ON ALL THE SPACE JUNK IN ORBIT—

160347

IF THE RED LIGHT GOES ON, GET OUTTA THE WAY—BUT DON'T GET UNDER _THAT_ TABLE...IT'S MINE!

It's big bird time, again. In the past your author has been accused of devoting too much space to fighter types. This should rectify this imbalance. (There's an ulterior motive, too. These behemoths fill space with less drawing!)

THERE ARE THREE STOCK PHONE ANSWERS TO A MAC AIRCREWMAN'S MOST FREQUENT QUERIES —

"THE CREW BUS IS ON ITS WAY"
"YOUR PER DIEM CHECK IS IN THE MAIL"
"YOU'RE THE **ONLY** ONE AVAILABLE"

There I Was…At Lackland AFB, "The Gateway to the Air Force." Here's where *70,000* recruits a year enter the Air Force. Being in Texas, naturally everything about the base is *BIG*, e.g., 1,000-man barracks where basics can march indoors in bad weather!

FIRST DOT (DAY OF TRAINING) INCLUDES THE "CLIPPER CUT" IN 90 SECONDS.

ON THE 14TH DOT, AIRMEN DON THEIR BLUES and STAND A LOT TALLER!

THE OBSTACLE (AKA "CONFIDENCE") COURSE SEPARATES THE MEN FROM THE BOYS — and THE WOMEN FROM THE GIRLS!

THE 5TH WEEK IS PARADE and GRADUATION DAY — THE TROOPS LOOK SHARP*

* THEY *HAVE* TO — THEY'RE GRADED BY MTI's TO THE GATE!

Air refueling takes special skills. Rough air, long orbit times, missed hook-ups, and extensive TDY build crew character. Both of these are true stories about KC-135 crews — long the backbone of the force.

There I Was...At Normandy on the 40th anniversary of the largest amphibious invasion in history. U.S. airmen rest side by side with thousands of their fallen fellow servicemen who led the assault to free Europe — it was a time for those who survived to honor those who did not.

"THANKS, BUDDY"

There I Was...At USAFE HQ, Ramstein AB, Germany. Just 7 min. by jet from the bad guys. USAFE units — 35 TAC Sqdns & 130,000 blue suiters — would be among the the first to meet 'em eyeball to eyeball. The CINC USAFE, who also commands Allied Air Forces, Central Europe (AAFCE) says "Our job is to fly, fight and *WIN!!*"

SHOULD THE SOVIETS THINK ABOUT PRESSING THE ISSUE, *1600* AIRCRAFT COULD LAUNCH FROM 70 PLUS BASES IN SHORT ORDER-IT'S ENOUGH TO MAKE ONE THINK TWICE!

HE JUST KEEPS LOOKING AT THAT USAFE/AAFCE MAP *and* MUMBLING "NYET, NYET"

TACTICAL UNITS, LIKE THE 526 TFS BLACK KNIGHTS (AKA "TINHEADS") *and* 512 TFS DRAGONS (AKA "LIZARDS") TROLL THE SKIES NEVER KNOWIN' WHAT THEY'LL SNAG...

LET'S SEE, IF THOSE ARE MIRAGES THEY'RE FRENCH. IF THEY'RE HARRIERS, IT'S THE BRITS. IF THEY'RE FGR-2s...

KNOCK IT OFF, BUSHEME, AN' CHECK 6!

AT DECIMOMANNU -"DUTCHY" FOR SHORT- DOWN IN THE MED MOST NATO FIGHTERS JOIN UP FOR A EUROPEAN "RED FLAG".

GEHEN SIE RUND! AB- FARHT!

MIO DIO! SALE E GIRA!

WHAT DID THEY SAY? WHAT DID THEY SAY?

I SAY, OL' CHAP, I DO BELIEVE THEY WANT YOU TO GO AROUND. IT SEEMS YOUR ALIGHTING GEAR'S NOT DOWN.

ITALIAN OWNED

PLANS CALL FOR USING THE GERMAN AUTOBAHN AS EMERGENCY LANDING STRIPS—

HEY! THAT GUY'S *PASSIN'* US IN A 500 SEL!!

In 1940, before the desperate days of the Battle of Britain, the Clayton B. Knight Committee (he of WW I Lafayette Escadrille fame) recruited U.S. pilots for the RAF. These volunteers later formed the legendary Eagle Squadrons.

WE ALL HAD A RATHER DISTORTED VIEW OF COMBAT LIFE IN ENGLAND—

ABBREVIATED PHYSICALS WERE USUALLY GIVEN TO RECRUITS IN POSH HOTELS AROUND THE U.S.—

PRE-SIGN-UP FLIGHT CHECKS WERE GIVEN IN ANTIQUATED U.S. BIPLANES—

THEN IT WAS OFF TO CANADA FOR "HARVARD" (T-6) TIME. IN THE U.K. ONE FERRIED HURRIES & SPITS BEFORE BEING POSTED FOR THE REAL THING—

Here's some flotsam and jetsam that floated up in the ol' idea file. Actually, we were cleanin' out the folder and thought these were too good to pass up. Enjoy!

THE ORI
(OR, A VISIT BY STARS and ZEBRAS)

"AN ORI IS A SITUATION IN WHICH YOU STOP DOING WHAT YOU'RE DOING IN ORDER TO SIMULATE DOING WHAT YOU WERE DOING SO THAT YOU CAN SHOW SOMEONE ELSE THAT YOU CAN SIMULATE DOING WHAT YOU WERE DOING AS WELL AS YOU WERE DOING IT BEFORE YOU WERE INTERRUPTED."

"AIRSICK & SCARED STIFF"
(OR, THE FIRST JET RIDE)

TAKE A POOR SLOB OFF THE STREET and SLAP HIM IN A SMALL, HOT, DE-COMPRESSION CHAMBER THAT REEKS OF KEROSENE and SUBJECT HIM TO...

A BONDAGE HARNESS FROM THE LOCAL S and M SHOP

A PLASTIC BUCKET THAT'S TOO TIGHT

40# ON HIS BACK

SUCKING O₂ THRU A HOSE.

FLASHING STRANGE PICTURES

NOW, JERK HIM AROUND IN 3 DIRECTIONS WHILE HE HEARS BEEPS, HUMS, THUNKS, and FOREIGN BABBLING VOICES...
CONVINCE HIM IF HE LOSES THIS GAME OF SPACE INVADERS, HE'LL BE FRIED ALIVE... *Think he'll be scared?*

SCENE: DARK and STORMY NIGHT OVER TEXAS. IP IS LOOKING FOR WANDERING CADETS AT 37,000 FT. IP BECOMES SURROUNDED BY LOSTNESS—

LAREDO TOWER, THIS IS SKOSH FOR A STEER TO HOME PLATE.

THIS IS LAREDO TOWER... IS THIS A PRACTICE STEER?

LISSEN, LAREDO... I DON'T PRACTICE AT NIGHT!

Crews of cargo/transport birds can get pretty bored on long hauls. Fiendish scenarios like the one depicted below kill time between reporting points… (Note: This routine calls for a john in the rear, like the ol' C-46's and 47's)

Fun and games time! We continue to be amazed & amused by the true (maybe *slightly* embellished) stories that come from our readers! The L-20 happening falls into the "classic" category —

SCENE: A SAC BASE SPORTING THE THEN-NEW B-47s WITH JATO (JET ASSISTED TAKE-OFF) BOOSTERS.

SHOOT! LOOKIT THOSE SHOW-OFFS WITH THEIR ROCKETS!

YEAH... an HERE WE ARE STUCK WITH THESE 6 !*n' L-20s!

I KNOW HOW WE CAN PUT THOSE CLOWNS DOWN!

NOW, WE'LL RUN THE IGNITER WIRES TO THE COCKPIT an...

BUT, HARRY.. SMOKE FLARES?

THEN, ON A DAY WHEN THE B-47 WING WAS IN FULL ARRAY ON THE RAMP, "RED DOG LEADER" LEAPED OFF!

SCRAMBLE ONE!

RONR

CAREFUL, HARRY, YOU'LL STALL OUT!

SEEN ON A LONG MAC HAUL

COMFY?

Truth is stranger (you know the rest). The story about the helicopter actually happened at Danang — and there's a couple of ex-airmen firsts around to prove it.

We heard this story after WW II "as gospel" from several sources. We'll admit it sure sounds far out, but even if fabricated, it still makes quite a tale.

This is a true story about "flying sergeants" (There were a lot of 'em in WW II — over 5,000, I think). Enlisted trainees went through the same program and wore the same uniform as aviation cadets — save for service caps. The one exception was the horse cavalry — they were, well, *different*.

There I Was…At sunny Davis-Monthan AFB, Az. "D-M" has 28 units representing *6* major commands! The 836th Air Division heads up the whole works, which includes A-10's, OA-37's, EC-130H's and various support units. Of all these systems, the A-10 is probably the one that could best be described as …ah… well, *different!*

A-10 PILOTS-HOG DRIVERS-AS THEY SEE THEMSELVES.

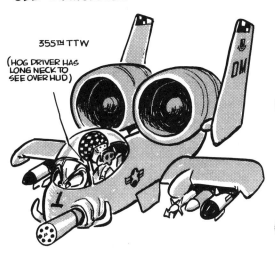

FLYING THE "THUNDERBOLT II" IS LIKE BEING IN A TIME WARP BACK TO WW II–

HOW SLOW IS THE WART HOG? IT'S **SO** SLOW THAT…

SPEAKING OF REFUELING, FAMILY ORIENTATION RIDES ARE STILL GIVEN IN THE A.F. ONE A-10 PILOT WAS HOOKED UP TO A KC-135 THAT CONTAINED-AMONG OTHERS - HIS WIFE.

...Roaming around Davis-Monthan AFB, Arizona, where I spotted some strange-looking birds. One appeared to be a derivative of the "Herky" — the other, an off-shoot of the "Tweety Bird". Closer examination revealed some startling differences.

THE EC-130Hs BELONG TO THE 41st ELECTRONIC COMBAT SQDN (THEY CONFUSE THE ENEMY'S DEFENSES *and* OUR OWN TRANSIENT ALERT CREWS)

WHAT DOES ALL THAT STUFF DO?

IT ACTS LIKE A DRAG CHUTE IF WE HIT ICING!

"FENCE"

"PLOW"

"TRAPEZE"

AT THE OTHER END OF THE FIELD IS THE 23rd TACTICAL AIR SUPPORT SQDN. THESE FORWARD AIR CONTROLLERS (FACs) FLY THE GUTSY LITTLE OA-37Bs.

HEY, GROUND, YOU SAY THE F-16s ABORTED? NOT TO WORRY, *I'M* ON STATION WITH A FULL LOAD!

2 T-38 ENGINES!

(2) 2.75 in. rocket launcher tubes - 7 ea.

(4) 600 lb fuel- or napalm tanks on pylons

PLUS (1) 45 cal. pistol strapped on pilot's side.

SPEAKING OF FACs, THE FOLLOWING TOOK PLACE AT A SPECIAL FORCES CAMP IN SEA...

THE FAC CALLS IN AN F-4 WITH A 2,000# BOMB.

WE'VE GOT A TANK TRYIN' TO CRUSH OUR BUNKER. WE NEED HELP!

O-2A

NO SWEAT! YOU'VE GOT "PAVE NAIL" HERE. STANDBY ONE...

WHAT THE HELLSA "PAVE NAIL"?

K A B L A M!

WOW! WHO, OR WHAT, DID YOU SAY YOU WERE??

PAVE NAIL!

TELL 'IM WE'D LIKE ABOUT 2 MORE!

U.S.

There I Was...At "Willy" — Williams AFB, Arizona — after an absence of *42* years! (I had graduated there, class of 43-E). It was spooky. Most everything had changed dramatically, but some things were just as they were in May, 1943.

It's back to "dirty-tricks-in-the-T-33" time. That grand ol' bird was designed with practical jokers in mind. This episode involving a smallish IP and behemoth AF R.O.T.C. cadets illustrates the point —

ORIENTATION RIDES - BIG SPRING, TEX.

YOU FOUR CADETS— I'LL TAKE YOU IN ORDER *YOU*, MISTER, GRAB YOUR GEAR!

(THE AGGIE FRONT FOUR. ALL 6'4" 3rd. 240 lb PLUS)

5'4" 140# SOAKIN' WET

AS SOON AS ALTITUDE PERMITTED, THE IP WOULD FLICK THROUGH A FAST AILERON ROLL WITH BOOST ON.

WOW!! NEAT, SIR!

WANNA TRY IT?

YES, SIR!

FA-18

THE IP TURNS OFF THE AILERON BOOST-

JUST MOVE THE STICK ALL THE WAY TO THE LEFT...

UNGH! GRUNT!

YOU'RE LOSIN' ALTITUDE-

PUFF PUFF

HELP ME, SIR! I'M LOSIN' IT!

I'VE GOT IT.

FLICKS ON BOOST

AND SO IT WENT, CADET AFTER CADET-

PUFF 'HOW DOES THAT LI'L ___ *DO* THAT ?

PANT

BEATS ME!

Gen. "Tooey" Spatz said it, "The B-17 is the greatest weapon man has ever built." The Forts *50th* birthday was celebrated at Boeing this summer! It was a fitting salute to a plane the free world should never forget —

THE '17 ENTERED COMBAT EARLY. PLANES DESTINED FOR THE 19th BG IN THE PHILIPPINES TOOLED INTO PEARL DURING THE SURPRISE ATTACK!

TORA! TORA! TORA!

HEY, NAV! YOU *SURE* THIS IS HAWAII? LET ME SEE THOSE MAPS!!

BUILT LIKE A TANK, THE FORT COULD ABSORB INCREDIBLE AMOUNTS OF FLAK *and* SURVIVE —

"WALK ON IT," HELL! ENGLAND, HERE I COME!

B-17 GUNNERS EXACTED A HEAVY TOLL OF ENEMY FIGHTERS - 23 PLANES PER 1,000 SORTIES —

WELL, YAS, WE *DID* RUN INTO A LI'L FIGHTER OPPOSITION...

AT THE BOEING ANNIVERSARY PARTY OLD CREWS *and* PLANES WERE REUNITED —

DAMN! I SURE DON'T REMEMBER THESE HATCHES BEING SO *6∹⁎ NARROW!

NO KIDDIN' GRANDPA! YOU FIRED FROM *THERE*?

There I Was…At Luke AFB, "Home of the fighter pilot" (Nellis makes the same claim — there's bound to be a shoot-out some day). Two of America's hottest fighters, the F-15 and F-16 work out in the hottest weather in the U.S. The result? Hot pilots ready to fulfill TAC's mission!

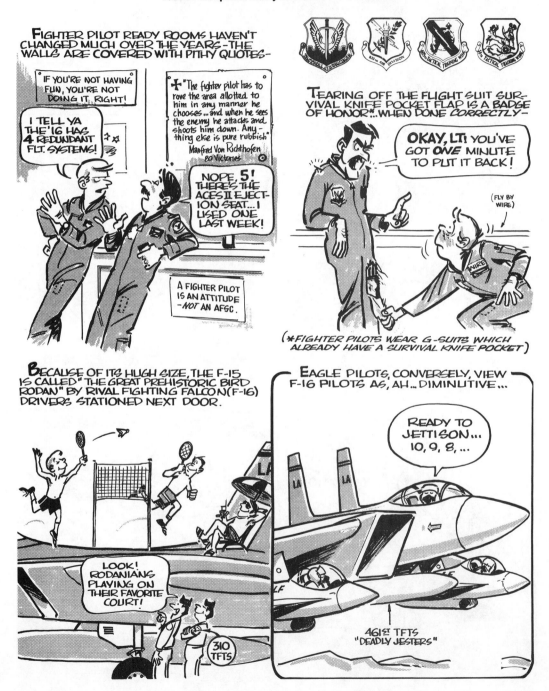

FIGHTER PILOT READY ROOMS HAVEN'T CHANGED MUCH OVER THE YEARS — THE WALLS ARE COVERED WITH PITHY QUOTES —

IF YOU'RE NOT HAVING FUN, YOU'RE NOT DOING IT RIGHT!

✝ "The fighter pilot has to rove the area allotted to him in any manner he chooses…and when he sees the enemy he attacks and shoots him down. Anything else is pure rubbish"

Manfred Von Richthofen 80 Victories

I TELL YA THE '16 HAS 4 REDUNDANT FLT. SYSTEMS!

NOPE. 5! THERE'S THE ACES II EJECTION SEAT…I USED ONE LAST WEEK!

A FIGHTER PILOT IS AN ATTITUDE — NOT AN AFSC.

TEARING OFF THE FLIGHT SUIT SURVIVAL KNIFE POCKET FLAP IS A BADGE OF HONOR*…WHEN DONE CORRECTLY —

OKAY, LT! YOU'VE GOT ONE MINUTE TO PUT IT BACK!

(FLY BY WIRE)

WIRE

(*FIGHTER PILOTS WEAR G-SUITS WHICH ALREADY HAVE A SURVIVAL KNIFE POCKET)

BECAUSE OF ITS HUGE SIZE, THE F-15 IS CALLED "THE GREAT PREHISTORIC BIRD RODAN" BY RIVAL FIGHTING FALCON (F-16) DRIVERS STATIONED NEXT DOOR.

LOOK! RODANIANS PLAYING ON THEIR FAVORITE COURT!

310 TFTS

EAGLE PILOTS, CONVERSELY, VIEW F-16 PILOTS AS, AH…DIMINUTIVE…

READY TO JETTISON… 10, 9, 8, …

461st TFTS "DEADLY JESTERS"

Gooney Bird, Dakota, Skytrain, Dizzy Three, Placid Plodder, Douglas Racer, C-47, R4D, Puff the Magic Dragon, or simply — "The three". That grand old lady of the skies, the Douglas DC-3 is *50* years old this month. At least 2 generations of Army/Air Force crewmen — and passengers — salute you, ol' gal!

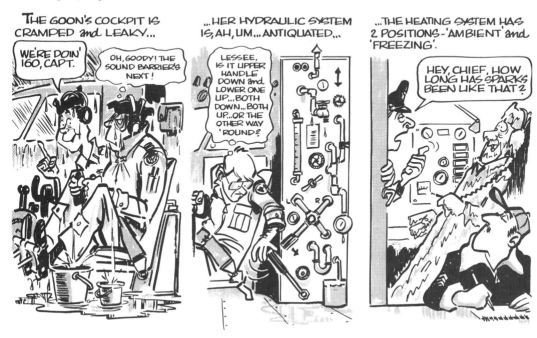

There I Was...Visiting AF Reserve outfits at Bergstrom AFB. The Air Reserve Forces make up *40%* of our total force! Surprised? We were! You can forget "Weekend Warriors" and hand-me-down equipment. These people are ready *NOW*... and with well-maintained machinery!

THE RESERVES HAVE DISHED IT OUT TO THE REGULARS SINCE DAY 1 (REMEMBER, "HERE'S TO THE REGULAR AIR FORCE ♪"?) THEY CAN ALSO LAUGH AT THEMSELVES.

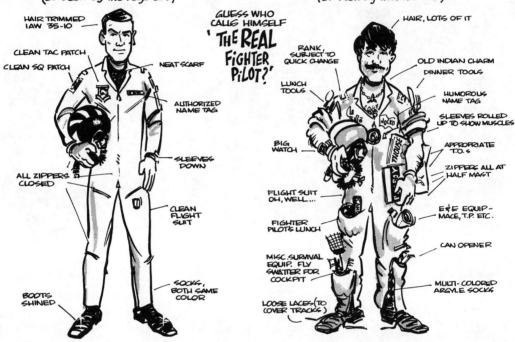

REGULAR AIR FORCE
(as seen by the regulars)

- HAIR TRIMMED IAW 35-10
- CLEAN TAC PATCH
- CLEAN SQ PATCH
- NEAT SCARF
- AUTHORIZED NAME TAG
- SLEEVES DOWN
- ALL ZIPPERS CLOSED
- CLEAN FLIGHT SUIT
- SOCKS, BOTH SAME COLOR
- BOOTS SHINED

GUESS WHO CALLS HIMSELF 'THE REAL FIGHTER PILOT?'

AIR RESERVE FORCES
(as seen by themselves)

- HAIR, LOTS OF IT
- RANK, SUBJECT TO QUICK CHANGE
- OLD INDIAN CHARM
- DINNER TOOLS
- LUNCH TOOLS
- HUMOROUS NAME TAG
- SLEEVES ROLLED UP TO SHOW MUSCLES
- APPROPRIATE T.O.s
- BIG WATCH
- ZIPPERS ALL AT HALF MAST
- FLIGHT SUIT OH, WELL...
- E&E EQUIP - MACE, T.P. ETC.
- FIGHTER PILOT'S LUNCH
- CAN OPENER
- MISC. SURVIVAL EQUIP. FLY SWATTER FOR COCKPIT
- MULTI-COLORED ARGYLE SOCKS
- LOOSE LACES (TO COVER TRACKS)

THE 704th TFS's "DOOFER BOOK"-THE EQUIVALENT OF A REGULAR OUTFIT'S "HOG BOOK"- COUGHED UP THIS BEAUTY:

THE *VERY* SMART BOMB:

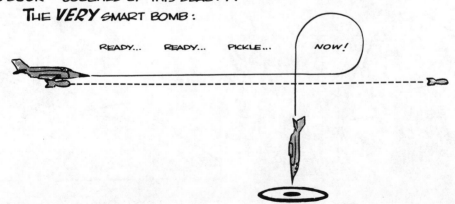

READY...   READY...   PICKLE...   NOW!

The best stories are true. The following in-flight refueling episode proves the point. Picture yourself over the mid-Atlantic during the early 1960's. You're in a flight of F-105's equipped with rather primitive Doppler navigation equipment and led by a know-it-all ace.

There I Was...Still prowling around the Air Reserve Forces. The 704th TAC FTR SQ, 924th TAC FTR GP (RES), is a red-hot F-4D outfit flying out of Bergstrom AFB near Austin, Texas. Like their regular brethren, 704th crewmen exchange a lot of flak between cockpits and the ground.

A PHANTOM II IS MAKING AN IFR APPROACH IN IFFY WEATHER—

WOOSO (Weapon Systems Officer) and BIB*

"STICK ACTUATOR" (Pilot)

HEY APPROACH! YA GOT US DOWN TO 175 KTS...DO YOU KNOW WHAT THIS AIRCRAFT STALLS AT ??

NO, BUT YOU COULD ASK YOUR WOOSO— HE MIGHT KNOW!

* BRAINS IN BACK

PILOT

LONGEVITY and EXPERIENCE...KEY WORDS... 15 YEARS IS THE *AVERAGE* FOR GROUND CREWMEN!

IT'S NOT OFTEN YA SEE *THAT*!

THAT'S HIS DAD. HE JUST BEANED HIM WITH A WRENCH!

924TH CAMS

(BEEN IN THE OUTFIT SINCE '69)

OLD WOUNDS HEAL SLOWLY. AROUND THE O'CLUB BAR YOU CAN HEAR BALLADS GOIN' BACK TO KOREA—

"HERE'S TO THE REGULAR AIR FORCE, WITH MEDALS & BADGES GALORE, IF IT WEREN'T FOR THE G--D--- RESERVISTS, THEIR ARSE WOULD BE DRAGGIN' THE FLOOR!"

SUNG TO TUNE "MY BONNIE LIES OVER THE OCEAN"

TRY iT

We've never featured that old SAC workhorse — the KC-97 (and many readers might be saying "Why bother?"). But those who flew the lumbering tanker during the waning days of the prop era in the 60's would agree the ol' girl deserves *SOME* recognition.

THE PILOT'S HANDBOOK DESCRIBED HER AS A "HIGH-SPEED, HIGH-ALTITUDE, LONG-RANGE TRANSPORT"

WHEN 20+ BIRDS FIRED UP AT ONCE, EXHAUST SMOKE PUT THE PLACE ON INSTRUMENTS!

YOU COULD ALWAYS RECOGNIZE THE CREWMEN WHO STOOD FIRE GUARD —

B-47 RECEIVERS WERE ALWAYS SCREAMING FOR MORE AIRSPEED DURING REFUELING —

Question: Can you identify the two aircraft involved in the last dogfight in Europe during WW II? Answer: An unarmed L-4 Cub and an armed (well, sort of...) German Fieseler "Storch" German observation plane.

SOURCE: "THE WW II QUIZ & FACT BOOK" P. 140 HARPER & ROW N.Y. © 1982 TIMOTHY B. BENFORD

They were called "Nipper", "Piddler", "Lightning", "Barney," and more often than not, "Sad Sack". These are the names given to mascots by airmen in virtually every unit since the First Aero Sq. was formed in 1913. Mascot population reached its zenith during WW II.

THE MAJORITY OF CANINES ADOPTED BY FLYING UNITS HAD THEIR OWN GEAR—

(IT HAPPENED TO A LOT OF TROOPS, PAL)

MOST EM'S DOGS HATED OFFICERS.

"NIPPER" OF THE 20th FTR GP.

IF MEMORY SERVES ME RIGHT, THERE WAS A '17 OUTFIT THAT HAD A SMALL DONKEY AS ITS MASCOT—

(IT WENT O'SEAS WITH 'EM!)

GREATEST MASCOT STORY: THE C-47 THAT BELLIED DEEP IN EAST GERMANY AFTER THE CREW HAD BAILED OUT LEAVING JUST THE MASCOT ABOARD*

There I Was...At AFA's "Gathering of Eagles" — 1986" The largest and most spectacular aerospace event ever held in United States! Three generations of airmen came together in Las Vegas, Nev., for a five-day exposition of airpower past, present, and future.

THE ROSTER OF ATTENDEES LOOKED LIKE THE "WHO'S WHO" OF MILITARY AVIATION-

HE JUST MET GENS. YEAGER, DOOLITTLE, LEMAY, GABREL, 2nd. STEVER... GIMME SOME MORE WATER!

REUNIONS OF OLD OUTFITS 2nd INDIVIDUALS WERE RAMPANT-

"TINY" TIMMERS! YOU HAVEN'T CHANGED IN 42 YEARS!

"EAGLE EYE" FENSTER

THE "THEN" WAS A CONFEDERATE AF WWII AIRSHO USING THEIR VINTAGE BIRDS-

NOLEN, JUST IMAGINE FOLKS ARE FILMIN' THIS ON THEIR SONYS!

VIRDEN

THE "NOW" WAS AN AWESOME DISPLAY OF CURRENT USAF CAPABILITIES BY TAC—

1 SEC. BURST, GAU-8 GUN.

BRRRRRRP!

HEY, FEARLESS, HOW'A LIKE TO BE A ROOSKIE TANK DRIVER?

AT THE GIANT CONVENTION CENTER, 150 INTERNATIONAL AEROSPACE FIRMS DISPLAYED THEIR WARES—

I KNOW ROBOTICS IS BIG, BUT IF HE ASKS YOU FOR A DATE AGAIN, I'M GONNA PUNCH HIS LIGHTS OUT!

TEC STAR

SYMPOSIA & MAJOR PANEL DISCUSSIONS DEALT WITH TIMELY MIL. AEROSPACE TOPICS-

TODAY: "DESIGNING TOMORROWS AIR FORCE"

SOME 7000 ATTENDEES FROM 54 NATIONS OGLED THE BEST IN THE WEST. THE FUTURE WAS THERE, TOO—

WO IST DER SCHTICK?

I COULDN'T HANDLE IT... DON'T GET A RELIEF TUBE!

F-16

F-117A

HONORS NIGHT PAID TRIBUTE TO THE DOOLITTLE RAIDERS, MEDAL OF HONOR RECIPIENTS, 2nd OTHER LUMINARIES...

HONEY, WHY DON'T YOU HAVE ONE OF THOSE PRETTY BLUE RIBBONS?

[TRUE STORY]

THE WIND-UP WAS A GALA SHOW LOADED WITH STARS-STAGE 2nd MILITARY.

THAT'S ONE FORMATION THAT WASN'T IN THE THUNDERBIRDS ROUTINE!

WHEN THE SHOW LIGHTS DIMMED 2nd ALL THE PARTICIPANTS DEPARTED, ONE STAR STILL SHONE 2nd GAVE A CLEAR MESSAGE TO OUR ENEMIES:

"BEWARE OF THE EAGLE IN DEFENSE OF ITS OWN."

The bon mots used below are taken from real-life experiences, exaggerated a bit maybe, but *real*. Proving, once again, that communication is the basis of most aviation humor. You'll note the majority of incidents involves night or weather... conditions that breed the garbled word.

KOREA-1952. A USAF NIGHT INTRUDER IS CAUGHT IN SEARCHLIGHTS & FLAK. THE CREW REACTS WITH ITS USUAL APLOMB—

NAVIGATOR TO PILOT, BREAK **LEFT**... **YOUR** LEFT... YOUR **OTHER** LEFT !!

THERE'S *ALWAYS* SOMEONE WHO DOESN'T GET THE WORD—

DARK LENS WORN 2 HRS BEFORE FLT. (FOR NIGHT EYE ADAPTATION

HEY, BLUE LEADER! THESE DAMN GLASSES DON'T HELP A BIT!

OKAY, ACE, YA FOUND THE RUNWAY- NOW HOW DO WE GET TO THE RAMP ?

DUDE 3, THIS IS LUKE SOF* UNDERSTAND YOU TOOK THE BARRIER. ANY OTHER PROBLEMS?

NONE WORTH MENTIONIN'

✷SUPERVISOR OF FLYING

As every combat pilot knows, radio silence is imperative over enemy territory. This minimizes the possibility of a radio "fix" and keeps the friendly's channel open for news bulletins — like "We're being bounced!" A true story:

Here's a belated tip of the visor to those unknown, unseen, & unsung GCI "scope dopes". In SEA, these pitiable mole-like creatures labored in dark rooms for up to 18 butt-numbing hrs per shift. They often had 40 acft on frequency, all BS-ing at once, four tankers, and a dozen receivers "under control..."

Windy and the flares — Pt I. "Windy" — the name has been changed for obvious reasons — was the embodiment of Joe Btfsplk (Al Capp's li'l guy with a black cloud over his head). In this true story, Windy has drawn runway supervisor duty at his F-4D base —

Windy and the flares -- Pt II. Remember "Windy" who scored a direct hit on a bomb trailer with a flare? We picked up the true story of our hapless hero once again in the Runway Supervisor Unit (RSU) — this time ready to launch the first flight of the day... are you ready for this?

TWO F-4s ARE COCKED and AWAITING A FLARE FROM THE RSU—

OKAY, WE GOTTA MILE VIZ. LAUNCH 'EM!

YES SIR!

(THINK OF THE RSU AS A GYM LOCKER WITH A GOLDFISH BOWL ON TOP)

SINCE IT'S FOGGY and COLD OUTSIDE, WINDY ELECTS TO FIRE THE FLARE FROM *INSIDE*—

AW #ⓖ★✺!!! THE GUN SLIPPED OUTTA THE PORT!

FLAREGUN PORT

KLUNK!

GUN TO FLARE: "WE HAVE IGNITION"

FLARE:

KA-BOOM!

ZIP

ZANG

THERE GOES WINDY - I GUESS WE'RE CLEARED...

ZZZZAP!

Like most "THERE I WASes", this story is true, a C-141 has followed a thunderstorm into an overseas base with a barely adequate runway. Mix a behemoth aircraft with minimal runway length, add water and...

One of the biggest obstacles standing between the USAF air crewman and clear, concise radio communications is the "wafer switch". This innocent-looking rotatable selector becomes a demon of modern science when left in the wrong position.

Most of the material shown every month in this feature is true... Rarely do we fabricate stuff. These stories come from *real* happenings to real folks. This true tale from a B-52 crew is typical and proves, once again, the Air Force is peopled largely by comedians —

CO-PILOT HAD HABIT OF CRACKING FLIGHT LUNCH BOILED EGG THUSLY:

TAP! TAP!

THEN ONE DAY... (TICKED-OFF GUNNER)

FRESH EGG

CO-PILOT'S LUNCH

AS "B" FOLLOWS "A":

WE CAME ACROSS THIS "BACK-UP WEATHER STATION" WHILE VISITING McCHORD AFB OPS. WE'LL LAY YOU ODDS THAT IT'S EVERY BIT AS ACCURATE AS ALL THAT SOPHISTICATED GEAR BACK IN THE MET OFFICE!

THE EQUIPMENT

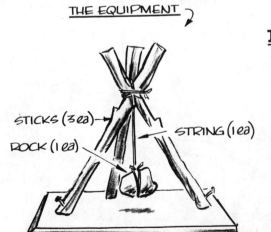

STICKS (3 ea)
STRING (1 ea)
ROCK (1 ea)
BASE BOARD

HOW TO INTERPRET OBSERVATIONS

IF ROCK IS:	IT'S:
WET	RAINING
WHITE	SNOWING
MOVING	WINDY
HARD TO SEE	FOGGY
CASTING SHADOW	SUNNY
COLD	CHILLY OUT
WARM	HOT OUT

PILOTS: TAKE THE GUESSWORK OUT OF WX BRIEFINGS – MAKE YOUR **OWN** STATION!

It was called "the forgotten war", a "U.N. police action", and a lot of unprintable things. Fact is, the Korean conflict (1950-53) clobbered about the same number of people in 3 yrs as 'Nam did in 12 plus. In this dirty, miserable war, jet combat came of age.

F-86 SABRES WERE BAPTIZED BY FIRE UP NEAR MANCHURIA'S YALU RIVER... IT WAS A *LONG* WAY BACK TO HOME PLATE –

MAYDAY! MAYDAY! KIMPO CONTROL, THIS IS BLINDMAN BLUE LEAD... I'M SHOT UP *and* FLAMED OUT!

RAAAJ, BLUE LEAD. YER NO. *2* IN THE PATTERN. NO.1 IS ALSO A FLAMEOUT!

THE RUSSIAN-BUILT MIG-15s WERE LIGHT & MANEUVERABLE... BUT ESPECIALLY LIGHT!

LT. COL. "RODE" RODEWALD

HEH HEH... GOTCHA NOW! ANOTHER 20 KTS *an'* THAT SPAM CAN'LL COME UNGLUED!

335 TH FIG INSIGNIA

B-26 "INVADERS" PROWLED NORTH KOREA BY NIGHT, DISHING OUT – *and TAKING* – A WHOLE LOT OF DAMAGE:

LOOKIT THAT! I TELL YA THAT ROUTE'S IMPOSSIBLE! FLAK *and* SEARCHLIGHTS EVERYWHERE!

YOU WERE PROBABLY TOO HIGH...

TOO HIGH? I WAS DOWN TO **50** FEET!

HELL, NO WONDER YOU GOT SHOT UP! YOU GOTTA GET DOWN *LOW* TO WORK THAT ROUTE!

Radar controllers scope undergrad pilot trainees to keep 'em in their designated area. When one appears to be wandering afield, he is told to "work north" (or south, etc.)". Normal radio exchange: (Radar) "Reese 23, say heading" (Student) "010" (Radar) "Work south" (Student) "Roger" —

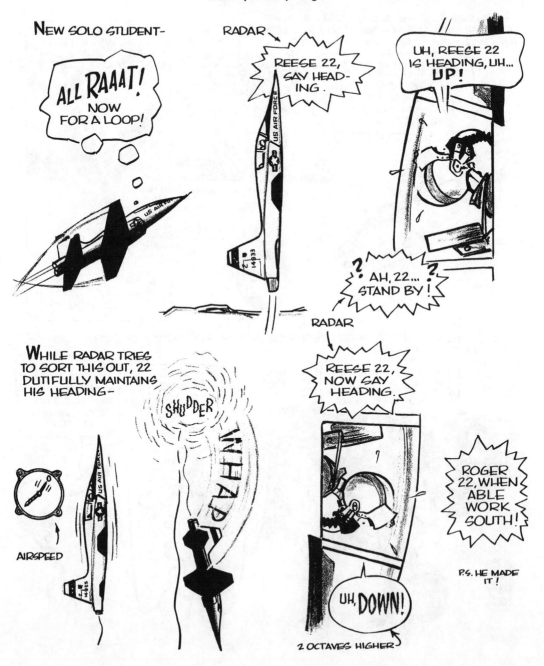

The bit below cried out to done in this space — flying or no. These are excerpts from actual letters received from mothers, wives and servicemen. They were either making or correcting applications for allotments of pay.

THE TIME : NOVEMBER 1944

" *Please send me my wife's form to fill out.*"

" Sir, I am forwarding my marriage certificate and two children, one of which is a mistake, as you can see"

" In answer to your letter, I gave birth to a boy weighing 101 lbs. I hope this is satisfactory."

" I want my money as fast as you can send it! I have been in bed with a doctor but he don't seem to be doing me much good."

We go back to WW deuce for these tales. There are many variants of the first story. We think this one — embellished somewhat — has the best ending.

SCENE: NEW AIRCRAFT, NEW CREWS EN ROUTE TO EUROPE-AN HOUR OUT OF THE AZORES.

HEY SKIPPER! A B-17 UP AHEAD!

LET'S PASS 'EM, CAPTAIN!

DIVE DOWN and FEATHER AN ENGINE!

SO THE '24 CRUISES BY THE '17 ON THREE ENGINES!

BYE, BYE! BUY BONDS!

OK, CAPT. NOW YOU CAN UNFEATHER IT

UNFEATHER IT, HELL! THE BUTTON'S STUCK!

IN A TOTALLY UNRELATED STORY WE HAVE THE CASE -NEAR WAR'S END- OF A HOT PILOT PARKING HIS BIRD WHERE HE SHOULDN'T OUGHTA –

...BUT, SIR, YOU CAN'T...

DON'T SWEAT IT, CORPORAL. I'M JUST AN R.O.N. and I GOTTA RUSH...HEAVY DATE!

BRAND NEW JUG

NEXT A.M.

SALVAGE AREA

History repeats itself. *Many* yrs ago we told the story of Nellis AFB's "Dusty" Rhoads (He wore a fishbowl in lieu of a helmet in an unannounced landing during an ORI at Biggs). Now, 20 plus years later another masked man steps forward. From Nellis, of course.

"Bedcheck Charlies" —night intruders — have made life miserable for people on the ground since air combat began. Sometimes they inflicted great damage, but more often than not they just bugged the hell out of you...

IN WWII WE HAD ONE CHARLIE WHO COULD **NEVER** SYNC HIS PROPS:

RRRRr ROWRRRRR

SNAG, YOU GOIN'TO THE SHELTER FOR THIS S.O.B.?

NAW, I'M PROTECTED 2nd HE HASN'T HIT ANYTHING, YET.

DURING KOREA, THE REDS USED THE VENERABLE Po-2 (CIRCA 1928) TO TERRORIZE THE TROOPS—

DIE, YANKEE DOGS!

BAZOOKA (NO KIDDIN')

5 CYL COUNT 'EM!

HAND GRENADE

TRYIN' TO NAIL ONE OF THESE GAD FLYS BLAZING ALONG AT TREETOP LEVEL AT 90 mph WAS ANOTHER THING—

YA OVER-SHOT, BOSS!

*#G! AH KNOW IT!! WE STALL AT 120!

F-82

WHOOSH

RADOME

POP

PUT

"BEDCHECK CHARLIE" LIVES ON AT THE AF ACADEMY WHERE HE MAKES HIS ROUNDS AT—AMONG OTHER PLACES—FALCON FOOTBALL GAMES.

WHO **IS** THAT MASKED MAN?

U.S. AIR FORCE

The Vultee BT-13 Valiant (AKA "Vibrator") was quite a flying machine. They built 11,537 of these trainers between 1939-'44. It had power (450 hp), was roomy (you could hear echoes in the belly pan), & its greenhouse canopy rattled like crazy — especially in spins. The flaps were hand-cranked, the prop was two-speed, and it had a *radio!*

Recently we flew with the 63rd Military Airlift Wing (MAC) out of Norton AFB. MAC has the largest airline in the country, and it runs a near-perfect schedule 'round the clock. The big C-141B Starlifter — workhorse of MAC — has a reliability rate of 95.8%! A figure that makes "scheduled" airline executives drool with envy!

This is the true story of a flight school instructor leading a first formation mission. The instructor had a short fuse & was called "The Screamer." This normally terror-filled experience was heightened when, unbeknownst to the leader, 3 seasoned instructors swapped places with the cadets — Here's "Left echelon, please!"

Have you ever wondered why *any one* would step out of a perfectly-running airplane a mile or so up? (Sport parachutists will give you a lot of screwy answers). *However,* when it comes to a crippled or mortally wounded bird, don't ask me "Why are we bailing out?" because you'll be talkin' to yourself!

The dollar nineteen, or C-119 (AKA "Flying Boxcar", "Crowd Killer", and other uncomplimentary names), was quite a work horse. She dropped hundreds, nay thousands, of paratroops and tons of supplies to beleaguered people worldwide. Here's a funny true story 'bout the ol' gal...

We go back to the Korean War, which — like 'Nam — was not popular at home. When the fertilizer hit the propeller, WW II vintage men and equipment were hastily thrown into the breach. There were bound to be some foul-ups...

Here we feature the B-36. Its 230 ft. wingspan qualified it as the biggest bird to see service in the USAF until SAC retired the last one in Feb. 1959. This aluminum overcast had six pusher prop engines and four turbojets on wing pods. Pilots often reported, "Six turnin' and four burnin'".

IT WAS A **BIG** MOTHER (SHIP)! OFTEN USED AS AN "OVERDRIVER" IN SECRET DRONE, TRAPEZE, and DROP TESTS—

PSST, YOUNG MAN. VITCH IST DER _FRONT_ OF DER AEROPLANE?

4925 TH TEST GP. (ATOMIC)

LOS ALAMOS PhD TYPE

THERE WAS AN 85-FOOT, PRESSURIZED CREW TUNNEL THRU THE BOMB BAY. (IT SEEMED A MILE LONG & ONE RODE A LITTLE PULL-ALONG SLED)

GUESS WE'D BETTER CHECK CABIN PRESS-URIZATION, CAPT.

VOOM!

AND WHAT A WAKE THOSE BRUTES LEFT AT 40,000' + IN SUPER-THIN AIR!

PILOT FROM LEFT SCANNER—WE JUST LOST CHASE ONE.

I'M STALLING OOUT

SNAP!

THIS BEHEMOTH NEVER DROPPED A BOMB IN ANGER... and AFTER ALL, THAT'S THE REASON WE HAD 'EM!

BUT THOSE **BIG** BUTTER PADDLE PROPS SCARED THE HELL OUT OF OUR OWN PEOPLE!

MOMMY, IS IT THE END OF THE WORLD?

THOB! THOB! THOB! THOB! THOB! THOB!

Not everything in this space is funny — you know, *FUNNY*, funny. This true story is, however, *interesting*. Besides being entertaining, it demonstrates American ingenuity — which, after all, was the "X factor" in winning many things we could have lost...

We dedicate this page to that recently retired old workhorse, the C-123 "Provider". Pilots in 'Nam called her the "Bookie Bird". She was no beauty queen, built from the plans of a defunct towed glider, she depended on two ol' R-2800 round engines to blaze along at about 125 kts!

Aerial refueling is not a stroll in the park! Add night, a combat zone and a rather green, new-in-SE Asia boomer and the procedure can become a frustrating one for a well-seasoned receiver...

The DOD has announced availability of the prisoner of war (POW) medal. There are an estimated 42,000 AF and former AAF personnel eligible for this highest of all service awards. In WW II, many folks at home had no idea of the deplorable conditions our POWs suffered. Sound like 'Nam and the POW/MIA situation?

BELIEVE IT OR NOT, THESE ARE *ACTUAL* EXCERPTS TAKEN FROM A POW's "A WARTIME LOG"*(STALAG LUFT I) 24 FEB 44-8 MAY 45.

"LETTERS FROM HOME"

* ORIGINALLY, A 150 pp. BLANK, BOUND BOOK (TO BE FILLED IN BY THE RECIPIENT) AS A "PERMANENT SOUVENIR OF THE PRESENT UNPLEASANTNESS", COURTESY YMCA, GENEVA.

When WW II hit, the U.S. needed aircrews — good ones — and we needed 'em *FAST!* The AAF projected an aviation cadet wash-out rate of 40 to 50% for those mentally and physically qualified. Our class (43E) washed close to 47%; 4021 entered in Aug. 42, and 1876 graduated May 20, 1943. A few of the survivors met in Phoenix on our 45th anniversary. Where, oh, where did all those young men go?

Humor is the secret ingredient in the substance of the U.S. fighting man. It — along with faith, good training and equipment — sustains him in some of the worst possible situations. Can you imagine prolonged nerve-tearing Persian Gulf duty without a touch of humor?

Here's what the new U.S. POW medal looks like. It's made of bronze and shows an eagle encircled by barbed wire —

RIBBON

MEDAL

FOR A LOOK AT WHAT MOST OF OUR POWs WERE THINKING ABOUT WHILE SURVIVING INCARCERATION, LET'S TAKE A PAGE FROM A KRIEGIE'S* DIARY, STALAG LUFT I, 1944 —

132

MAX C. BLOOM'S
KRIEGIE SHOPPE
Announcing a new line of
ESCAPE ACCESSORIES

Newest SPRING ESCAPE ENSEMBLE
EXTRA!

• OVERSIZE POCKETS FOR CANNED FOOD OR "D" BARS.

VERY SPORTY!
GUARANTEED
TO PASS AS A
CIVILIAN!

PRICE
100 CIGS (ED. NOTE: CIGARETTES WERE USED IN PRISON BARTER SYS)

TRAINED!
TUNNEL DOGS

PEACHY FOR YOUR NEW SPRING TUNNEL!

LOW SLUNG

BIG TEETH FOR EXCAVATION

LARGE TONGUE FOR EARTH REMOVAL

AN EXCELLENT PET WHEN NOT IN USE!!!

A **BARGAIN** AT 69 CIGS!

WIZARD

WIRE CUTTERS
(BOOK OF INSTRUCTIONS INCLUDED)

KRIEGIES SAY:

THEY'RE PRIMA!

ASK THE KRIEGIE WHO OWNS ONE!

only 29 CIGS!

PASSPORTS

PLUS RAILWAY TICKETS OUT OF EUROPE VIA THE MOST SCENIC ROUTES!

see

GERMANY - FRANCE
SWITZERLAND - HOLLAND
SPAIN - ITALY
NORWAY - SWEDEN

DURING YOUR ESCAPE

* GERMAN FOR "WAR PRISONER".

In the old days, thoroughly reading tech manuals *BEFORE* check-out was considered unsporting by a few of the crews (pilots were often accused of just getting in and pushing buttons until something meaningful happened). This is a true story…

It has been my great privilege and honor to draw this feature for 25 years. It seems appropriate to look back at four reprints representing distinct periods in AAF/USAF history that we've shared during the past quarter century.